MOONSCAPE

PITTED DOMES RISE UP FROM THE FLOORS OF GREAT WALLED CRATERS; SHADOWLESS WHITE "RAYS" STREAK ACROSS VAST DISTANCES; ROCK MOUNTAIN-CHAINS TOWER TOWARD INFINITY. OVER THE MOON'S DUST-COVERED SURFACE A MYRIAD STRUCTURE OF TINY FAIRY CASTLES, BUILT FROM HARDENED DUST PARTICLES, REFLECT LUNAR LIGHT BACK TO EARTH.

In this intriguing book Willy Ley gives a detailed account of the lunar facts uncovered by modern spacecraft investigation. Beginning with the legends and theories of antiquity, through the scientific findings of Galilei, Kepler, Newton, and winding up with the 1964 moon probes, the pioneer in rocket research and the world's leading authority on space travel interprets and explains what science has learned about the moon. Mr. Ley gives a fascinating description of the mysterious red spots, the newest theories about the moon's origins, dramatic reconstructions of actual space flights as he takes the reader through space on a RANGER TO THE MOON.

Other SIGNET SCIENCE LIBRARY Books

RANGER
TO THE MOON

Willy Ley

A SIGNET SCIENCE LIBRARY BOOK
PUBLISHED BY THE NEW AMERICAN LIBRARY

SIGNET TRADEMARK REG. U.S. PAT. OFF. AND FOREIGN COUNTRIES
REGISTERED TRADEMARK—MARCA REGISTRADA
HECHO EN CHICAGO, U.S.A.

*SIGNET SCIENCE LIBRARY BOOKS are published by
The New American Library of World Literature, Inc.
501 Madison Avenue, New York, New York 10022*

TB 6/15/81

PRINTED IN THE UNITED STATES OF AMERICA

Table of Contents

Text Illustrations

Picture Section

1. The moon, region of the *Mare imbrium*. The large dark-floored crater near the bottom of the picture is Plato; to the left of it are the lunar Alps with the Great Valley. The crater with prominent later-impact craters inside its ringwall (near the left edge of the picture) is Cassini. The four craters lying across the *Mare imbrium* in a nearly straight line are, left to right: Autolycus, Archimedes, Timocharis, and Lambert. The crater below Autolycus is Aristillus. The solitary crater with a central peak near the upper right-hand corner is Eratosthenes. The mountain above Plato is Pico. As in all astronomical photographs, south is at the top. *Mt. Wilson and Palomar Photograph*

2. "Sunrise on the Moon." An example of what the moon does *not* look like. The craters are not the towering ramparts shown, and if somebody should discover soaring spires like those in the background, the surprise would be great. *(French illustration, c. 1880)*

3. The mountain Pico, in the *Mare imbrium*, as drawn by James Nasmyth.

4. Small cinder cone on earth. James Nasmyth's drawing of a small volcanic mountain at the end of a street in Tenerife. He considered it quite similar to the much larger Pico in the *Mare imbrium*. Many astronomers now assume that the mountain peaks on the *mare* plain, such as Pico, Pitom, and the Straight Range, are only the tops

of much larger mountains that were tall enough to reach above the lava flow producing the *Mare imbrium*. This question can be decided only by investigation on the spot.

5. The crater Copernicus, as drawn by Edmund Neison (c. 1875). Riccioli, who admired the Danish astronomer Tycho Brahe and did not have much use for Copernicus and Kepler, gave all three names to craters on the moon. But he wrote, "I flung Copernicus and Kepler into the *Oceanus procellarum.*" In spite of this dismissal, astronomers have considered Copernicus the most beautiful and most typical of all lunar craters and have lavished infinite care on mapping it.

6. Copernicus. Photograph of model made by James Nasmyth (c. 1870).

7. Copernicus, as drawn by the British astronomer Thomas Gwyn Elger in March, 1889. Elger reported that under exceptional seeing conditions he could count dozens of minute hillocks on the crater floor. But even when seeing conditions were at their best, he could not make out what they were.

8. Copernicus, as drawn by Philipp Fauth (c. 1920).

9. Copernicus through the 200-inch. To the left of Copernicus a string of craterlets *almost* forming a "rill" can be seen, as well as a so-called ghost crater. *Mt. Wilson and Palomar Photograph*

10. Meteor Crater, in Arizona, also known as Barringer Crater, was the first impact crater on earth the true nature of which was recognized by the mining engineer and geologist Daniel Moreau Barringer of Philadelphia. *Photograph: Dr. Clyde Fisher*

11. The dead volcano Hverfjall, on Iceland, a perfect picture of a basal wreck. Note similarity to Meteor Crater (Plate 10).

12. Impact-crater models and the lunar crater Theophilus. Top left: impact crater with central peak; top right: im-

pact crater without central peak; bottom left: impact
crater made of plaster of paris; bottom right: the lunar
crater Theophilus, to the left of it the smaller but deep
and obviously recent crater Mädler. The three models
were made by the author in the manner described in the
text; they were photographed under slanting sunlight
without previous hardening. Their actual diameters var-
ied between three and four inches.

13. Takeoff of the Atlas-Agena rocket that carried Mariner
    VII to the moon. *Courtesy: NASA*

14. Ranger, with folded solar panels. It was in this position
    that Ranger rode, protected by a "shroud," into space as
    payload of the Atlas-Agena rocket.

15. Ranger as it must have looked while in transit to the
    moon after the shroud had been thrown off and the solar
    paddles had unfolded. If this were actually a flight picture
    the sun would be above the picture's top, the moon to
    the right, and the earth to the left. The motion, of course,
    would be in the direction of the moon. *Courtesy: NASA*

16. One of the first pictures transmitted back to earth by
    Ranger VII in the morning hours of July 31, 1964. The
    spacecraft was 1,163 miles from the lunar surface at that
    moment. The width of the area photographed is 260
    miles. The large crater with a central peak and a small
    impact crater next to it (upper-left-hand corner) is Ar-
    zachel, the smaller crater with a central peak next to it is
    Alpetragius (both named after Arab astronomers), and
    the large and shallow crater adjoining them is Alphonsus
    (named after a king of Spain). The large shallow crater
    near the lower-right-hand corner is Guericke, named after
    the burgomaster of Magdeburg who proved the existence
    of air pressure—something that does not exist on the
    moon. Impact took place in the vicinity of the black
    cross (part of the measuring grid) near the center of
    the picture, fifteen minutes and a few seconds after this
    picture was transmitted. South is at the top. *Courtesy:
    NASA*

17. Sequence of Ranger photographs. (Distances given always
    refer to the distance between the camera and the features

photographed, not to the height of the Ranger spacecraft above the lunar surface at the moment. Because of the slanting approach, the height above the moon and the distance to the photographed object were not quite the same.)

A. A section of the surface of *Mare nubium* from 84.9 miles. Watch the group of small secondary craters above the center of the picture.

B. Same, from 60.9 miles; the cluster of small secondaries has now moved to the center.

C. Same, from 53.5 miles; many smaller craters begin to appear in the cluster.

18. A. Distance is now 44.8 miles; the number of discernible craters is still growing.

B. Distance is down to 28.6 miles; there are still more small craters.

C. Distance is now only 20.4 miles; the small craters now can be seen to be "soft" because of the steady rain of nearly microscopic particles.

19. Just before impact. The upper picture was taken by the F-a camera at an altitude of about three miles. One side of the picture corresponds to a distance of 1⅔ miles on the moon. The three-hundred-foot crater with the angular rock mass mentioned in the text is near the upper-left-hand corner. Smallest craters visible in this picture are about thirty feet across. The lower picture was taken by the P-3 camera from a height of one thousand feet. Spacecraft crashed before transmission was completed; therefore about two thirds of the picture is "snow"—receiver noise. Smallest craters in this picture are about three feet across and about one foot in depth.

20. Close-up of the six television-camera lenses that took the pictures of the lunar surface. *Courtesy: NASA*

21. Lunar orbiter in orbit around the moon. (Composite photograph of a prototype model of the orbiter and a model of the moon.) *Courtesy: The Boeing Company*

22. A scene from *The Girl in the Moon*. The film *Frau im Mond*, to give it its original German title, was released on October 15, 1929. It was the first major movie to deal

with space travel and was also the first to have scientific advisers. The scene shows the top stage of the moon rocket soon after landing on the moon's far side. For dramatic purposes it was assumed that humans could breathe in the moon's atmosphere. *Courtesy: Fritz Lang and Cinécothèque française*

23. Another scene from *The Girl in the Moon*. The flight path of the movie spaceship shown was calculated by Professor Hermann Oberth and bears an astonishing similarity to the flight path envisaged for the Apollo spacecraft. (The actress is Gerda Maurus.) *Courtesy: Fritz Lang and Cinécotèque française*

24. The LEM (lunar-excursion module). This photograph shows a so-called mock-up, a full-scale model, usually made of wood. But the finished spacecraft will look hardly different from this mock-up. *Courtesy: Grumman Aircraft*

25. The LEM on the moon. The lower part, the octagonal box with the four landing legs, will be left behind on the moon. Only the upper portion will return to orbit and join the orbiting command module. *Courtesy: Grumman Aircraft*

Foreword

A number of years ago, during late summer and fall of 1948, I wrote a rather successful book entitled *The Conquest of Space* in which I spoke of the three eras of astronomy. The first era was the one that began in ancient Babylonia—or earlier—and which lasted until the first decade of the seventeenth century. During this era the word "observation" meant looking at the sky. At later dates during that era some "instruments" were added, first the cross-staff and later quadrants and sextants, all of them devices for measuring the angle between two stars or the angular distance of a star from the horizon.

The second era began around the year 1608, when Hans Lippershey in the Netherlands put the first telescope together. The invention was so simple that others could do the same at a moment's notice; as a matter of fact Galileo Galilei in Italy stated later that he built his first telescope "in a single night." The statement is not only credible, it would have been astonishing if it had taken him longer. A friend of his had written him from Paris that a new invention had been made, consisting of two lenses in a tube and that such a tube made distant objects look near. All that Galilei had to do was to find out at which distance his available lenses had to be mounted to produce this effect.

Just as some instruments were added to the naked eye during the first era of astronomy, some additional instrumentation was added to the telescope during the second era, the most important being the spectroscope and the photographic plate.

But while the telescope and the astronomical camera did wonders in revealing the surface features of some planets and of the moon—especially of the moon because of its relative nearness—they also discovered a number of mysteries. We could see and photograph features of the lunar surface. But we could not explain them, or else three different observers could think of three different explanations, which is about as illuminating as having no explanation at all. These mysteries, as I wrote over fifteen years ago, will not be explained until the third era of astronomy dawns, the era of spacecraft, which will bring us to the spot of investigation.

Of course I was asked quite often how long it would be, in my opinion, until the third era of astronomy would begin. My answer was "ten or twelve years," but after some time I began to add "under the assumption, of course, that there is an active project for doing it." However, for more years that can be justified, there was no active project and consequently it took longer than a dozen years.

The first sign of a dawn of the third era of astronomy came on September 1, 1959, when the payload and the upper stage of a large Russian rocket struck the moon. The amount of new knowledge produced by this shot was fairly small, but it proved that one *could* get a device from the earth to the moon. Since then a Russian rocket has succeeded in taking a number of pictures of portions of the far side of the moon and two American devices have struck the moon, but without adding to our knowledge. But on July 31, 1964, at the time when it was morning along the eastern seaboard, day broke for the third era of astronomy. During that morning Ranger VII transmitted over four thousand close-up pictures of the lunar surface.

Considering what is bound to come in the third era of astronomy, the pictures taken by Ranger VII can well be compared to the drawings of the lunar surface made by Galileo Galilei in 1609. But the fact that he could make these drawings showed that a new era had begun, and the pictures taken by Ranger VII have the same meaning.

WILLY LEY

October 15, 1964

RANGER

TO THE MOON

1. Names, Names, Names...

A few years from now a manned spacecraft will be purposefully drifting through space along a trajectory carefully calculated to reach the only natural satellite of earth. While the ship is on its way to the moon, some of the astronauts inside will get ready to land on the lunar surface, and after their mission has been accomplished the results will be compiled by the official *selenographer*.

Why three different words? Simply because three different languages are involved, or rather the names for the moon in three languages. The Latin name for the moon was *"luna,"* and all the current languages which sprang from the original Latin still use variations of the word (if Commissaire Maigret should happen to look at the moon during one of his night vigils he would think of it as *la lune*). All the Germanic languages use names that can be easily recognized as variations of the English "moon." But the name of the moon goddess among the Greeks of antiquity was Selene (pronounced say-lay-nay); hence the imagined inhabitants of the moon were referred to as selenites and a description of the moon was called a selenography.

Since the moon changes its appearance in a regular sequence, all early peoples used it to establish a time interval of greater length than the simple day that was counted either from sunset to sunset (in the Middle East) or from sunrise to sunrise (in northern Europe). This longer time interval, from the first appearance of a thin lunar crescent in the evening sky to the next crescent, is of course the month. Thus it is not an accident that the words for moon and for month are nearly the same. This holds true in many languages: the German word for "moon" is *"Mond"* and the word for month is *"Monat";* in Russian the word *"mésyats"* means both "moon" and "month," though the Russians, when referring to the moon as an astronomical body, use the Latin name with a shift in accent (*"luná"*).

During the first era of astronomy, when the observer's eye was not yet aided by optical instruments, the moon was not only a convenient changing light for measuring time but also of special interest because it was the only thing in the sky which showed spots. And it did not need many moons of observation to tell that these spots changed neither their extent or shape nor their relative positions. That fact, of course, required an explanation, and the obvious answer was that there were probably mountains and valleys and lakes on the moon which presented themselves to our eyes as varying shades of light and dark. But speculations of how the lunar landscape might look to an observer on the moon were of interest only to very small circles of learned men.

Folktales about the moon grew up everywhere and were much more colorful. In France the dark spots were believed to be the image of Judas Iscariot, transported to the moon as punishment for his treason. In Germany the "man in the moon" was an old man bent down by the weight of a load of firewood which he had picked up in the forest on Palm Sunday morning, when he should have been in church. In another German version the spots of the moon show an old woman knitting stockings. In India the spots were thought to be a leaping buck or a leaping hare, and the Russians never pretended to see anything in the moon but a human face. The Russian fairy tales have the interesting twist that the moon, seeing the whole earth at night, would necessarily know where things are, and for that reason Ivánotchka Durajók, the recurrent simpleton of Russian folktales, often asks the moon to tell him where the captured prince is hidden or where the treasure is kept.

One pretelescopic speculation about the moon survived for a long time in Persia, as is known from a chance event. A little over a century ago the German naturalist and traveler Alexander von Humboldt resided in Paris for a number of years and made the acquaintance of a well-educated Persian from Isfahan. Learning that the Persian had never looked through a telescope, Alexander von Humboldt took him to the observatory and aimed the telescope at the moon. The explanations he was about to give were waved aside by the Persian, who declared, "What we see in the moon is ourselves; it is a map of the earth." Humboldt, taken aback, asked his visitor how he knew this and the Persian said that this was a common belief in his country. The reason that Von Humboldt was so surprised was that this idea, that the spots on the moon are the mirrored oceans and continents of the earth, was well known to him as a Greek idea ascribed to Clearchus and reported by Plutarch.

When Galileo Galilei began looking at the moon he saw to his surprise that there were very many smaller spots which nobody had ever been able to see. In order to distinguish his newly discovered small spots—the ones that came to be called "craters"—from the dark naked-eye spots, he called the latter the "ancient spots." The brighter areas of the moon were pitted with craters, and mountain chains and valleys were clearly visible, but the "ancient spots" were quite smooth, so Galilei decided that they were water and referred to them as *maria,* or seas.[1] Later they received individual names, as listed in the table on page 23. But Galilei's search of the heavens with a telescope had produced another result: he discovered that the planet Jupiter was accompanied by four large moons.[2] This fact called for a new term. Up to that point only the earth had been known to have a moon and it had its name. But since Jupiter had moons too and the other planets therefore could be suspected also to have moons, it was desirable to have a general term for the moons of planets to avoid confusion.

The German astronomer Johannes Kepler, who was living in Austria at the time, supplied such a general term in a personal letter he wrote to Galilei in 1610. He suggested the word "satellite," derived from the Greek word *"satellos,"* which means "attendant."

It seems somewhat strange that Galilei only drew sketches of the moon and never combined them into a real chart. Whether he decided to leave this task to later astronomers who might have better telescopes or whether he simply did not have the time because of his many other activities is

[1] The Latin word for "sea" is *"mare,"* pronounced MAH-ray; *"maria"* is the plural, pronounced MAH-ree-ah.
[2] It is now known that Jupiter has twelve moons. Galileo Galilei discovered the four largest: Io, Europa, Ganymede, and Callisto. Ganymede and Callisto have diameters of 3,200 miles, while the diameter of Io is 2,300 miles. Only Europa, with a diameter of 2,000 miles, is smaller than our own moon, which measures 2,160 miles.

something we don't know. The first to make a chart of the moon was Professor Cesare Lagalla in Rome in 1612. The second man to draw such a chart was the Flemish mathematician Michael Florent van Langren, who was employed at the court of King Philip IV of Spain. His map was ready in 1628 and it showed an innovation: names began to be scattered over the surface of the moon. That the surface features had to be named for easy reference was obvious; the problem was what names should be used. Langrenus (as he called himself) was in favor of biblical names such as "King David's Mountains" and "Solomon's Sea." Others did not go along with this suggestion, provided that they had seen a copy of Langren's map (it was printed in 1645), which is by no means certain.

The German astronomer Johannes Hewelcke (better known as Hevelius, the Latinized version of his name) gave the problem some systematic thought. It was tempting to name lunar features after famous men, philosophers such as Plato and Aristotle and astronomers such as Copernicus and Kepler. But Kepler had died only recently, and it was only too likely that somebody would give the name of a living

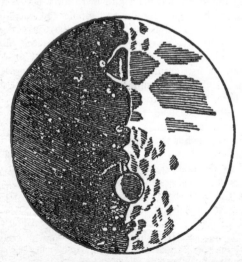

Fig. 1. Drawing of the Moon by Galileo Galilei (1610). The picture clearly shows a large crater and several "rays," but there is no agreement on the identification of these features.

NAMES OF THE LUNAR FEATURES VISIBLE
WITH THE UNAIDED EYE
(SO-CALLED "SEAS")

LATIN	ENGLISH
Mare imbrium	Sea of Showers
Oceanus procellarum	Ocean of Storms
Mare serenitatis	Sea of Serenity
Mare tranquillitatis	Sea of Tranquillity
Mare foecunditatis	Sea of Fertility
Mare nubium	Sea of Clouds
Mare nectaris	Sea of Nectar
Mare humorum	Sea of Moisture
Mare crisium	Sea of Crises
Mare frigoris	Sea of Cold

The following features are of the same type, but are not naked-eye objects. They are all located close to the rim of the visible hemisphere.

Mare australe	Southern Sea
Mare smythii	Smyth's Sea
Mare marginis	Marginal Sea
Mare novum	New Sea
Mare humboldtianum	Humboldt's Sea

friend to a mountain on the moon. If that happened the door would be opened to all kinds of petty jealousies and rivalries. There might then be lunar charts in which identical features had different names applied to them. (One wonders whether Hevelius' worries about jealousies and rivalries was not influenced by the fact that he was a member of the city council of the city of Danzig.) Therefore his own chart, printed in 1647, was as neutral as possible: the mountains of the moon were labeled with the geographical designations of mountain chains on earth. One chain he named the Lunar Alps, another the Lunar Apennines, still another the Lunar Caucasus, names that are still in use.

But there simply were not enough well-known geographical names and the names of people had to be attached to lunar formations. Of course everybody realized that there was danger in using the names of still living persons and to this day it is a rare event if somebody has his name attached to a lunar crater while still alive.

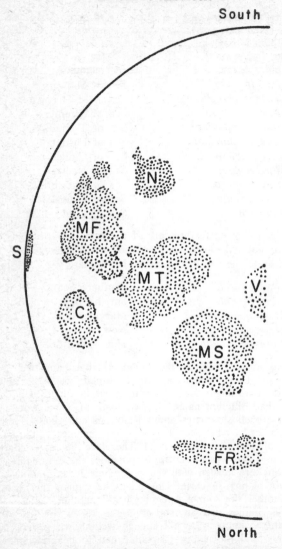

Fig. 2. The Dark Areas of the moon
OP—Oceanus procellarum   MT—Mare tranquillitatis
MI—Mare imbrium   MN—Mare nubium
MS—Mare serenitatis   FR—Mare frigoris
MF—Mare foecunditatis

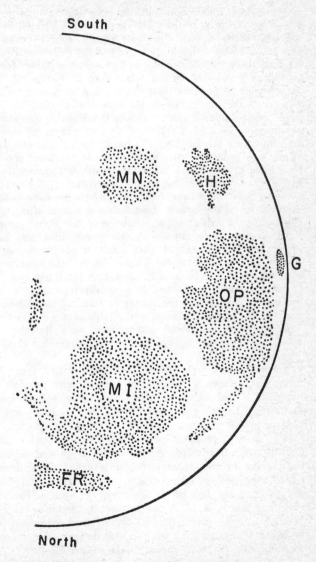

South

MN   H

G

OP

MI

FR

North

H—Mare humorum   S—Mare smythii
C—Mare crisium   V—Mare vaporum
N—Mare nectaris   G—(Walled Plain) Grimaldi

The turning point came with the book *Almagestum novum* ("The New Almagest"), by Giovanni Battista Riccioli, which was published in 1651. A chart of the moon, drawn by Francesco Maria Grimaldi, was part of the book and Riccioli supplied the names, especially to craters, since names for the mountain chains and for the *maria* were already in use. It is an oft-repeated assertion that the less a man had to do with astronomy the bigger the crater named after him. The two large craters, named after Plato and Aristoteles (Aristotle), are usually cited. Plato's contribution to astronomy was nil and Aristotle's contribution was hardly larger. But the assertion is not generally true. Riccioli named the most conspicuous lunar crater Tycho (after the Danish astronomer Tycho Brahe) and gave the names of Copernicus and Kepler to two very beautiful craters. Astronomers have not done badly in general; one of the largest lunar craters is named after Father Christopher Clavius, papal astronomer to Pope Gregory XIII. Another early astronomer, Longomontanus, also has a rather large crater named after him. Of course the largest craters were named first and Riccioli felt that the famous men of antiquity should be honored first. It is for this reason that classical names are attached to especially prominent craters, but many of them are the names of classical astronomers— such as Harpalus, Eudoxos, and Ptolemaeus (Ptolemy), to name only a few. Arab astronomers were honored too, usually with the Latin version of their names—for example, Albategnius.[3]

Riccioli's book says clearly (and for the first time) that there is no water on the moon, but the term *"mare"* was retained; it had merely shifted from being an attempt at description to being a useful label. The same applies, of course, to the so-called "bays" too. The Latin for "bay" is *"sinus,"* and there are a number of formations with names starting with this word. An especially large and beautiful indentation of the *Mare imbrium* is called *Sinus iridum,* which translates as "Rainbow Bay." Nearer the north pole of the moon, in the area of the *Mare frigoris,* we have the *Sinus roris,* the "Dewy Bay." A few features too small to be called *"mare"* bear the prefix *"lacus,"* "lake." *Lacus somniorum* is an example, though this name is a little difficult when it comes to translation. It really means "Lake of the Sleepers," since

[3] Since the full name of this Arab scientist was abu-'Abdullâh Muhammad ibn-Jâbir al-Battânî, one can understand why the Latin version was used.

"*somnium*" means "sleep," but "*somnium*" implies "dreams," hence the more customary translation is "Lake of the Dreamers." A few areas seemed to be marshy to early ob-

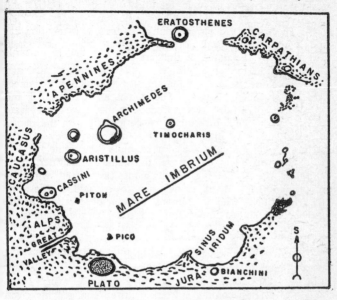

Fig. 3. *Mare imbrium,* Surrounded by Mountains. This is the largest of the dark areas on the visible hemisphere of the moon. Craters like Plato, Aristillus, Archimedes, and so forth are evidently younger than the *mare* plain, but the *Sinus iridum* represents the remains of a crater older than the *Mare imbrium.*

servers, hence their names begin with the word "*palus,*" which means "marsh," or "swamp." An example is *Palus nebularum,* the "Misty Swamp," not far from the crater Cassini, another crater named after a famous astronomer.

The scheme of naming lunar features, then, is the following: A large dark area, one of the naked-eye objects which Galilei called the "ancient spots," is called a "*mare,*" with a specific name. A smaller dark area, if attached to a *mare,* is a "*sinus*"; a similar smaller dark area, if not a part of a *mare,* is a "swamp," or "*palus.*" Craters are named after famous people. Large mountain chains bear the names of terrestrial mountain chains. Those surrounding the *Mare imbrium,* going clockwise beginning with the *Sinus iridum,* are the

Alps, the Caucasus, the Apennines, the Carpathian, and finally the Jura mountains, which partly surround the *Sinus iridum.*

Two other types of lunar features, the rills (or clefts) and the so-called "rays," do not as a rule have names of their own. The rills are deep canyonlike fissures, and the rays are long white streaks. Both normally originate from a crater and are called by the name of that crater.

In addition to *maria,* craters, mountain chains, rills, and rays there are isolated mountain peaks, which are named, and the so-called "domes." The domes are quite small and for that reason a fairly recent discovery; they have no separate names but in the future might be designated with the names of astronauts and lunar explorers. At present they are described by their location, as for example "the dome in Darwin," Darwin being, of course, the name of a crater.

Since we are talking about names associated with the moon, another set of names has to be added, those of the astronomers who are famous for their observations of the moon. It is almost unnecessary to add that their names do not appear only on and in books but on the lunar surface too.

The next astronomer after Riccioli and Hevelius to produce a map of the moon was Giovanni Domenico Cassini, who was astronomer at the court of Louis XIV of France and who after becoming a French citizen changed his given names to Jean Dominique. Cassini had various sections of the moon sketched by an assistant and an artist hired for the purpose and then combined them into a chart with a diameter of twelve feet. Then he called in an engraver, who reduced the chart to a copper plate twenty inches in diameter. Strange to say, Cassini dropped the work as soon as the plate was ready, and prints of that plate became available only long after his death. The next moon specialist after Cassini (who lived from 1625-1712) was a German, Tobias Mayer (1723-1762), who discovered the libration of the moon, which will be explained in the following chapter. He produced a chart of the moon eight inches in diameter that in spite of its small size was considered the best chart for many years to come. Sir William Herschel (1738-1822), who was the greatest astronomical observer of his time, did engage in lunar observations for a while, but then became intrigued with stars, double stars, and the probable shape of the galaxy and never returned to lunar studies, possibly because they had been performed diligently and

competently by his younger contemporary Johann Hieronymus Schröter (1745-1818).

Schröter, who had his own observatory in Lilienthal, near
Bremen, produced excellent lunar charts which were published in 1802. After Schröter's death several other Germans
took over, the most successful ones being a two-man team in
Berlin. The team consisted of the astronomer Johann Heinrich von Mädler (1794-1874) and the banker Wilhelm
Beer (1797-1850), who was an enthusiastic amateur astronomer and, incidentally, the brother of the composer Giaco-
mo Meyerbeer. Their three-foot chart of the moon appeared
in 1834. At the same time, Wilhelm Gotthelf Lohrmann
(1796-1840), who was a surveyor by profession, worked on
a map of the moon that was printed long after his death
because of the insistence of Julius Schmidt (1825-1884),
who also had made a lunar map. Lohrmann's map consists
of twenty-five charts, and current German astronomers still
think so highly of it that they had it reissued in 1963 as a
tribute to the memory of Lohrmann.

The published map by Julius Schmidt is not as good as
Lohrmann's because it is unwieldy in size and suffers the
drawback that not a single name appears on it.

After mapping the moon had been a kind of German
monopoly for three quarters of a century, the British took
over. A beautiful book on the moon by James Nasmyth (an
engineer) and James Carpenter (an astronomer) appeared in
1874. The book was illustrated by careful photographs of
models of many lunar features, carefully built for the purpose. Two years later followed a book on the moon by
Edmund Neison (1851-1938), who stated that he wished to
bring Mädler's chart up to date. His book consists of twenty-
two detailed maps of sections of the moon's surface, with
careful description of all named features.

By that time American astronomers appeared in the picture too. Simon Newcomb (1835-1909), for many years
astronomer at the U.S. Naval Observatory, made many detailed observations and Professor William Henry Pickering
(1858-1938) published the second photographic atlas of the
moon in 1903. The work was a little more ambitious than
the instruments of the time could accomplish. The first photographic atlas of the moon was published in 1896 in Paris
by M. Loewy and P. Puiseux, of which an enlarged and
revised edition appeared in 1899 in Brussels.

Probably the most active moon specialist in Germany
during the first part of the twentieth century was Philipp

Fauth (1867-1943), who unfortunately got his name involved in a pseudoscientific fantasy known as the World Ice Doctrine; for this reason his sound work on the moon did not receive as much recognition as it should have. Most active in England was H. Percy Wilkins (1896-1960), who produced a three-hundred-inch map in 1946 and a one-hundred-inch map in 1952. Another photographic atlas of the moon was published in 1959 by Gerard P. Kuiper and his colleagues at Yerkes Observatory. The biggest and most ambitious mapping project now underway is that of the U.S. Air Force, which is likely to undergo constant revision because of pictures of the moon taken quite close to the moon by orbiting television cameras.

2. The Orbit of the Moon

It is now almost precisely three centuries since the great English physicist and mathematician Sir Isaac Newton began thinking about the motions of bodies in space. By then it was already known that all the planets described orbits around the sun, and because of the patient (and endless) calculations of Johannes Kepler it was even known what the shape of these orbits was.

Tradition, before Kepler, had insisted that planets moved along circular paths, and when it became clear that this idea did not agree with observation, it was still assumed that the motion of a planet was along combinations of circular paths. Johannes Kepler was the first man who dared to think otherwise. He had inherited a stack of very accurate astronomical observations from the Danish astronomer Tycho Brahe and was determined to find a shape for an orbit that agreed with these observations. For a while he guessed that planetary orbits might be ovals, or, since this word is derived from the Latin word *"ovum,"* for "egg," that they might be egg-shaped. Kepler very quickly realized that this was not so, but to this day one can read in newspapers that an artificial satellite was put into "an egg-shaped orbit." This statement is not only wrong, it is also something that simply cannot be done.

Kepler then found that the true shape of a planetary orbit is an ellipse, a geometrical figure which has a number of interesting peculiarities. It does have a center, of course, but it also has two so-called focal points, which lie on its long axis equidistant from the center. The distance from one of these two focal points to a point of the periphery and from there to the other focal point is always the same, no matter which point of the periphery you pick. Or, to phrase this a little differently, if you construct triangles with the section of the

31

major axis between the focal points as the base line and the apex of the triangle anywhere on the ellipse's periphery, the sum of the three sides of any such triangle will be the same, no matter how the triangle is shaped. Kepler's fundamental statement, usually called Kepler's First Law, was that the orbit of a planet is an ellipse and that the sun is located in one of the two focal points of this ellipse.

This was the knowledge available to Newton when he began his own reasoning; he also knew that observation agreed with Kepler's ideas, so there could be no doubt about the facts. But Newton wanted to know *why* the facts were what they were.

Gradually he became convinced that gravity, the force that made an inkwell fall to the floor if pushed off the edge of a writing desk or that made a ripe apple fall out of a tree, was also responsible for the motions of bodies in space. This was in itself a new thought; most of Newton's learned contemporaries thought that gravity extended only a short distance beyond the cloud layer. But the thought itself contained a number of side issues. If gravity was responsible for the motion of a planet, just how did a body as enormous as the sun act on the planets? Was all the "attractive power"

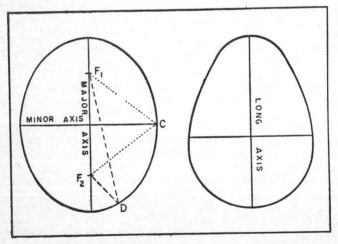

Fig. 4. Ellipse and Egg Shape. The ellipse is symmetrically halved by both the major and minor axes; the egg shape can be symmetrically halved only in one direction. In the ellipse the distance F_1 to C to F_2 is equal to the distance F_1 to D to F_2.

concentrated in one place or was the action more diffuse? Newton checked into this problem first and proved that the sun's gravitational pull acted as if the whole mass of the sun were concentrated in one point, namely, its center.

The next thought was that there had to be a second force which prevented gravity from ruling without any restraint. If gravity were the only acting force in space, the planets would have fallen into the sun, and the moon crashed into the earth, a long time ago. Newton found the answer in what has been known ever since as inertia. "Every body," he wrote, "continues in its state of rest or of uniform motion in a right [meaning "straight"] line unless it is compelled to change that state by forces impressed upon it." He then showed that an orbit existed because of the steady interplay of the inertia of a moving body and the gravitational pulls to which it is subjected.

Students of physics who now read Sir Isaac Newton's *Principia Mathematica* (first published in its original Latin in

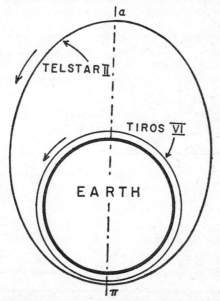

Fig. 5. The orbits of Telstar II and of Tiros VI, drawn to scale. The Greek letters α (alpha) and π (pi) indicate perigee and apogee. For actual distances see text.

1687 and published in English translation two decades later) are invariably surprised to see that Newton explained the motion of our own moon by first explaining the orbit of an assumed artificial satellite. Because the orbit of our moon presents a number of difficulties, it is practical to follow his example and to talk about artificial satellites first. The only difference is that we have actual artificial satellites that we can use as examples, while Newton had to assume one and probably never thought that his assumption would one day be carried out.

The two actual artificial satellites that will illustrate the principles and problems involved are the weather-watching satellite Tiros VI and the communications satellite Telstar II (Fig. 5).

Tiros VI was put into orbit on September 18, 1962. The point of its orbit nearest to the ground, the perigee, is 425 miles above sea level, while the point farthest from the ground, the apogee, is 442 miles away, a difference of only 17 miles. Since the diameter of the orbit of Tiros VI is about 8,800 miles, this orbit can be considered circular for practical purposes. Telstar II, fired on May 9, 1963, was put into a fairly elongated orbit, with a perigee 603 miles from the ground and an apogee at a distance of 6,712 miles. It is a

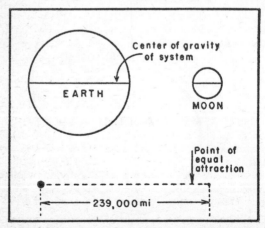

Fig. 6. Earth and Moon Drawn to Scale. The diagram also shows the positions of the center of gravity of the earth-moon system and the point in space where both will exert equal attraction on a space vehicle.

typical elongated ellipse, and that brings up the question of how the degree of elongation of an ellipse can be measured and described.

It is done by comparing the length of the major axis of an ellipse with the distance between the two focal points. Let us use the orbit of Telstar II as an example. The major axis of its orbit, from perigee to apogee, measures:

	perigee distance	603 miles
+	diameter of earth[1]	7,915 miles
+	apogee distance	6,712 miles
		15,230 miles

The distance of one of the focal points from the end of the major axis can be determined with equal ease. The focal point coincides with the center of the earth; therefore:

	perigee distance	603 miles
+	one earth radius	3,957 miles
		4,560 miles

Since one half of the major axis of the ellipse is 7,615 miles in length, the distance of the focal point from the center of the ellipse is 7,615−4,560=3,055 miles. The other focal point lies at the same distance from the center, so that the distance between the two focal points is 6,110 miles. This is just about forty percent of the length of the major axis, and the orbit of Telstar II therefore has an eccentricity of 0.40. If the distance between the two focal points amounted to one half of the length of the major axis the eccentricity would be 0.50.

Using the same method for calculating the eccentricity of the orbit of Tiros VI, we find that the length of the major axis is 8,782 miles and the distance of the two focal points from each other is a mere 18 miles, producing an eccentricity of 0.02.[2]

The figures about the orbit of our moon will be more meaningful after this explanation. They read: distance at perigee 221,463 miles, distance at apogee 252,710 miles,

[1] This is an averaged figure; the earth's polar diameter is 7,902 miles, while the equatorial diameter is a little larger, 7,928 miles.
[2] If the two focal points coincide, the eccentricity is zero and the figure becomes a circle, which is the reason that mathematicians say that the circle is only a "special case" of an ellipse; a layman might think that it is the other way around, because in everyday life circles are so common.

length of major axis 475,000 miles, distance between the focal points 26,000 miles, eccentricity 0.055.

So far everything is nice and simple. But now we get into a few complications, most of which are due to the fact that our moon is a fairly large body.

The perigee and apogee distances just quoted follow the astronomical usage of measuring from the center of one body to the center of the other body. Normally there is no difference worth mentioning between center-to-center and surface-to-surface distances. The planet Mars for example can approach the earth as "close" as thirty-five million miles. At that moment an observer on earth looking at Mars is a little closer, since he is not at the center of the earth. The combined radii of earth and Mars amount to about six thousand miles, but compared to the distance of thirty-five million miles these six thousand miles simply do not matter. But in the case of the moon there is a noticeable difference. Suppose that the moon is at perigee (221,463 miles center-to-center) and the observer is at the earth's equator, with the moon directly overhead. Half of the equatorial diameter of the earth is 3,964 miles, while half the diameter of the moon is 1,080 miles, hence the surface-to-surface distance at that moment is 5,044 miles less than the center-to-center distance, or a little more than two percent of the distance involved. It is not enough to influence observations, but it shows that in the case of our moon—and our moon only—a distinction between center-to-center and surface-to-surface sometimes has to be made. It has to be taken into consideration, for example,

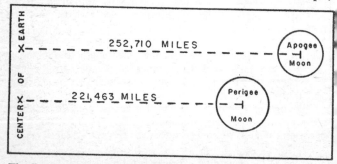

Fig. 7. Apogee and Perigee Distances of the Moon. At perigee the disk of the moon is larger than at apogee; the difference in size is shown in the diagram. But since the moon cannot present itself in both positions simultaneously, it needed astronomical photography to prove it.

when it comes to calculating the impact point of a rocket fired to the moon.

The comparatively large size of our moon also has another result, namely, that the focal point of its orbit does *not* coincide with the center of the earth. In the case of all artificial satellites the focal point around which the satellites revolve is the center of the earth, because the mass of even the biggest artificial satellite is negligible when compared to the mass of the earth. But the mass of the moon is not negligible. It is only 1.2 percent of the mass of the earth, but that is enough to move the focal point of the orbit. It does not coincide with the earth's center but is located in the common center of gravity of both bodies.

To understand what this means, let us for a moment assume the mass of both bodies to be equal. In that case the common center of gravity would be halfway between the centers of the two bodies and both would revolve around that point. The situation can be directly compared to a balance with equal weights at both ends. But since the mass of the earth is much larger than that of the moon we have the case of a balance with unequal weights at both ends. In

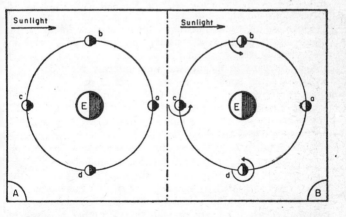

Fig. 8. How the Moon Turns on Its Axis. In diagram A, at left, it is assumed that the moon does *not* turn on its axis. If that were the case we would see one hemisphere when it is in position *a* and one half of a hemisphere in positions *b* and *d*; in position *c* it would be invisible. Diagram B, at right, shows the true situation. The moon has made a quarter turn in position *b*, half a turn in position *c*, and three quarters of a turn in position *d*. In position *a* it returns to the original position, after one full turn.

that case the balancing point moves toward the more massive of the two weights.

The balancing point, meaning the common center of gravity, of the earth-moon system is about three thousand miles from the center of the earth. This is still inside the earth, roughly one thousand miles below the earth's surface along the center-to-center line. The moon revolves around this point and so does the earth. But since the common center of gravity is still inside the earth, the earth does not describe an orbit around this point as it would if it were located one thousand miles above the earth's surface. The earth's motion is only a kind of wobble. If you pierce an orange with a long pin off center and then rotate the orange on this pin you have an indoor demonstration of this effect.

Of course this wobble has nothing to do with the daily rotation of the earth around its axis (which does go through the earth's center); it is an additional motion which is completed in the same length of time the moon needs to complete one orbit around the earth.

The mutual gravitational tugging between moon and earth has more results than just making the earth wobble a little on its orbit around the sun. The moon's gravitational pull raises the tides in the earth's oceans. To anyone who has seen the tide coming in while standing on a jetty it looks as if the moon must produce a veritable mountain of water in the ocean. In reality the tidal bulge caused by the moon is just about one yard in height; the tremendously high tides that can be seen in some places are the result of the funneling effect of converging coastlines, as for example in the Bay of Fundy. The effect of the earth's gravitational field on the moon has produced a far more profound result after hundreds of millions of years: it has slowed down the moon's original rotation to the point that the moon now rotates on its axis only once for every revolution around the earth.

The result is that we always see the same hemisphere of the moon if we look at it from earth.[3] Everybody knows that the moon, when full, always presents the same appearance, and everybody has also heard or read that the other hemisphere cannot be seen. But while these facts are known, they have caused several misconceptions. Quite a number of people are convinced that the moon has a "dark side" and that we cannot see it "because it is in darkness." Their mistaken

[3] Our moon is not unique in this respect. All the planets which possess moons have produced the same result; the moons in our solar system all rotate just once per revolution.

reasoning goes about as follows: if the moon looks only like a thin crescent to us, the invisible portion is the "dark side." If we had a searchlight powerful enough to illuminate the moon and if we trained that searchlight on the invisible portion while the moon is a crescent, we would see the features normally hidden from us.

It is an interesting thought which would be a powerful stimulus to the designers of searchlights if it were true. In reality such a searchlight would only reveal those features which we would see anyway if we waited for a week. When the moon is a crescent the invisible portions merely happen to be in darkness, but they are the ones we know.

The other misconception lies in a doubt whether the statement that the moon rotates once a month is correct. It seems at first glance that the moon should not rotate at all on its axis to produce the effect we see.

The best cure for this misconception is a little experiment involving a bright lamp in some corner of the room, a table (preferably a round one), and the doubter. The bright lamp in the corner is the distant sun, the round table is the earth,

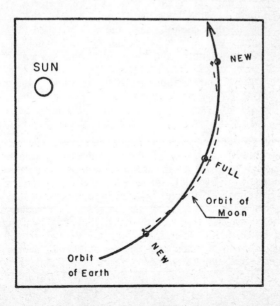

Fig. 9. The Orbit of the Moon Around the Sun

and the doubter is the moon. The doubter's task is to describe one orbit around the earth, that is to say, to walk once around that table. If he walks around the table in such a manner that he keeps his eyes on the lamp all the time he would not rotate on his axis, but a person squatting on the table would first see the doubter's face, then his profile, then the back of his head, then his other profile, and finally his face again. But if the doubter walks around the table keeping his eyes on the table, the watcher would see only his face all the time, but the doubter would also turn on his axis once while circling the table. And that is what our moon does.

Or rather this is the principle of the moon's rotation. In reality there is an additional phenomenon, the one discovered by Tobias Mayer and called "libration." Mayer noticed that a certain surface feature, say, a conspicuous mountain, did not seem to be at precisely the same distance from the moon's edge (astronomers refer to the edge as the "limb") all the time and he began to measure those distances. It did not take long for him to discover that there was a kind of pendulous motion; sometimes mountains or dark areas became visible at the eastern limb at a time when known features at the western limb became invisible. If one mapped the eastern features while they could be seen and then mapped the western features when they were visible, one could map a little more than just half of the moon, fifty-nine percent of its surface, to be exact.

The cause of the libration is that the rotation of the moon is uniform; as the moon turns on its axis a point of its equator will always move at the rate of 10½ miles per hour, never more and never less. But the rate of the motion of the

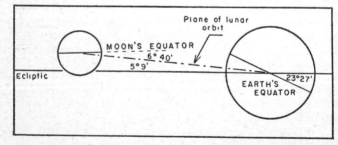

Fig. 10. Inclination of Lunar Orbit. The plane of the orbit of the moon shows an inclination of a little more than five degrees of arc to the plane of the earth's orbit. The lunar equator, however, is nearly parallel to the ecliptic.

moon on its orbit is not uniform; when closest to the earth (at perigee) it moves at the rate of 0.686 miles per second, but when farthest from the earth (at apogee) the rate of motion is only 0.60 miles per second. In order to show us precisely one half of its surface, the moon should turn a little faster on its axis when in the perigee section of its orbit and it should turn a little more slowly when in the apogee section. Since its rotation is uniform, we see a little of the area that should be beyond the limb when it is near perigee and we see a little of the area on the other side when it is near apogee.

Even though the difference between perigee distance and apogee distance amounts to a little more than 31,000 miles, a drawing of the moon's orbit in a book of normal size will always be a circle. The deviation of an ellipse of such small eccentricity from a circle is hardly more than the thickness of the line. But for every such drawing it is silently assumed that the earth is standing still. As we all know, the earth is in motion too, and for that reason the orbit of the moon is not the closed curve shown in all the diagrams. The real situation is shown in Fig. 9, illustrating a portion of the moon's orbit *around the sun*. It is far more correct to say that the earth and the moon both orbit the sun at an average distance of ninety-three million miles and that their orbits are intertwined.

It is the relative position of the earth and the moon while they are orbiting the sun that determines the phases of the moon. Of course the sunward hemisphere of the moon is always illuminated; the point is how it looks when seen from earth. If the moon is farther away from the sun than the earth, we see all of the illuminated hemisphere and we say that we have a full moon. When this is the case, it is night over the "far side" (the invisible hemisphere) of the moon. When the moon is closer to the sun than the earth, its far side has daylight while the familiar hemisphere has night and the moon is all but invisible. It can sometimes be seen because there will be a "full earth" over the night side of the moon and we can sometimes see a reflection of the earthlight. If the moon crosses the earth's orbit, we see half of the moon's daylight side and half of its night side and we have a half-moon in the sky.

The fact that the moon is sometimes about a quarter of a million miles closer to the sun than the earth, and sometimes farther from the sun by the same amount, accounts for the last phenomenon still to be discussed, namely, the eclipses. When the moon is "new," meaning that it is closer to the sun than the earth, its shadow may fall on the earth and we have an eclipse of the sun. Conversely, when the moon is "full" and farther from the sun than the earth, the earth's shadow may fall on the moon and we have an eclipse of the moon. But if this is the case, why don't we get an eclipse of the sun every time the moon is "new" and an eclipse of the moon every time it is "full"?

The answer is that we would get just such a regular succession of eclipses if the orbit of the moon had the same position as the orbit of the earth. If we draw a circle on a piece of paper and say that this is the orbit of the earth, the sheet of paper represents the plane of the earth's orbit. It has a special name: the ecliptic. Of course there is also a plane of the orbit of the moon, but this plane and the ecliptic do not coincide. They are inclined to each other slightly, by a little more than five degrees of arc (Fig. 10). Since this is a very

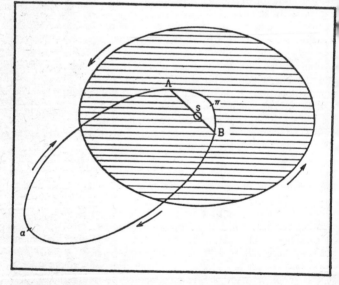

Fig. 11. Comet Orbit with High Inclination. The shaded ellipse is the plane of the earth's orbit, the ecliptic. The orbit of the comet is around the sun too, but only that section of the orbit near its perihelion is "above" the ecliptic. The two points A and B are the "nodes"; the line from A to B is the "nodal line." The position of the sun is marked by S; aphelion and perihelion of the comet's orbit are marked by the Greek letters α (alpha) and π (pi), as customary.

slight inclination, Fig. 11 shows the inclinations of the ecliptic and the orbit of a comet; comets often have very high inclinations. This figure shows clearly how part of the comet's orbit is "above" the ecliptic and another part is "below" it. The two points of the comet's orbit which lie in the ecliptic are technically known as the "nodes," and the line connecting them is logically called the "nodal line."

Naturally the moon's orbit, since it is inclined to the ecliptic, also has two nodal points and a nodal line. But the moon's nodal line does not remain in a fixed position. The orbit of the moon is rather complicated as it is, and the

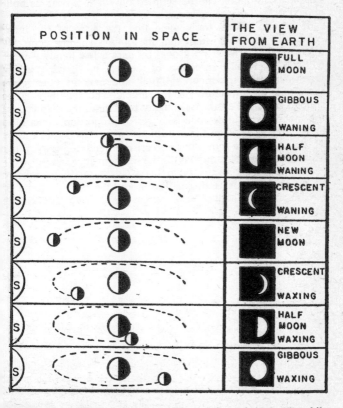

Fig. 12. The Phases of the Moon. The sun is at the left (S) while the earth is in the center of each position. Positions shown in space result in the visual appearance to an earthbound observer shown at right.

varying gravitational pulls of the earth and of the sun (and even of the planet Venus) cause the nodal line to shift slowly around the sky. It makes a full circuit in a little more than eighteen years. The wandering of the lunar nodes across the sky is the reason why we don't get an eclipse of the sun every time the moon is closer to the sun than we are. The moon can be in the "new-moon" position far from its node and it can be in the "full-moon" position while the other node is way off to one side.

Only when the moon is "new" *and* going through its node can its shadow fall on the earth, thereby eclipsing the sun. Likewise, the moon can be eclipsed only if it is near its node and "full" at the same time.

It is not difficult to imagine that the node of the lunar orbit is in such a position that the moon's shadow cone will just miss the earth. Even a miss by only a few hundred miles will fail to produce an eclipse of the sun, but if the situation is reversed and the moon is "full" and near its other node there will be an eclipse of the moon. The reason is quite simple: since the earth has roughly four times the diameter of the moon, its shadow cone is larger in proportion, covering a larger area. Therefore the conditions for producing an eclipse of the moon are not quite as critical, and logically lunar eclipses are more numerous by far than solar eclipses.

But while it is necessary to know all the complications of the lunar orbit for getting to the moon, the real mysteries of our neighbor in space are not in its motion but on its surface.

3. Craters, Rays, Domes, and Mountains

Since that night in 1609 when Galileo Galilei first saw his "new spots" on the moon, nearly seven hundred of them have been considered to be conspicuous enough to be given names—ten times as many as all other named features of the lunar surface. The reason is simple: the "new spots," or craters, are the most numerous feature of the surface.

While the *maria* are larger and some of the other features are more mysterious, any discussion of the moon's surface has to begin with the craters because of their vast numbers. In fact we'll never be able to tell just how many craters there are on the moon. They are not distributed in a pattern that would make counting easy, nor are they neatly placed side by side, even if in an irregular manner. In some places they are spaced reasonably apart, but in a very large area—the whole southern portion of the moon—they are incredibly crowded. Craters overlap, small craters can be found inside large craters, the ringwalls of large craters are interrupted by other craters, and older craters have been all but obliterated by more recent ones: it is one vast jumble that makes counting nearly impossible.

But this is only the beginning of the troubles for anyone who insists on statistics and is willing to make his own if nobody else did. Naturally the largest craters could be seen with small and rather weak instruments; equally naturally more and more craters appeared in the field of vision with every improvement of the resolving power of telescopes. Astronomical photography increased their number still more, and in 1935 it was estimated that one should be able to count about thirty thousand of them on the best photographs of the visible part of the moon. Under the assumption that the invisible portion looked more or less like the visible portion, the total number of craters would have been fifty thousand.

In 1935 there were only a very few people who considered it likely that cameras could be carried to the vicinity of the moon to photograph craters too small to show up in even the most powerful telescopes. Now, less than three decades later, this has been done successfully and we *know* that there is no lower limit to crater sizes; statistics will have to stop with an arbitrary lower limit.

Since lunar craters come literally in all sizes, older attempts to distinguish craters by coining different terms for different sizes are fairly meaningless. But the terms have survived because they are not completely useless. Craters of a diameter of more than a hundred miles were called "walled plains," and if it should be announced that a rocket on a photographic mission has secured pictures of several walled plains on the moon's far side, one would at least know from the term itself that they are very large. Craters less than a hundred

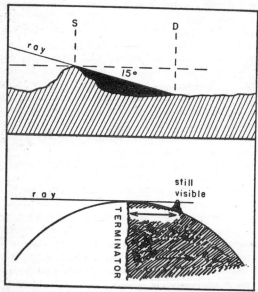

Fig. 13. Two Methods of Measuring the Height of Lunar Mountains. Top: The length of the projection of the shadow, *S* to *D* is measured; since the elevation of the sun is known, it is easy to calculate the height of the mountain. Bottom: A mountain peak on the night side of the moon is still visible because the sun's rays still strike its summit. Here the distance of the illuminated point from the terminator is measured.

miles in diameter down to about twenty miles were simply
called craters, though a few astronomers preferred the non-
committal term "ringwalls." Small craters came to be called
craterlets. There is no rule that states just what size they have
to have to be called that; the word merely indicates that they
are small and usually unnamed for that reason.

Quite a number of the smallest craterlets appear as
black holes and there is no way of measuring, or even of
estimating, their depths. But all the large craters are surprisingly shallow; they are round depressions below the general
level of the lunar surface with a not particularly high ringwall
as their boundaries. The crater Ptolemaeus, for example, has
a diameter of ninety miles and its ringwall is around a mile in
height. An astronaut who has landed in the middle of Ptolemaeus would not even be able to see the ringwall surrounding
him and his ship, partly because on the smaller moon the
horizon is much closer than it is on earth. What this astronaut
would see in the distance would probably look like one of
the mesas of the American Southwest to him. It would be the
small crater Lyot, which is located inside Ptolemaeus.

During the last decade of the eighteenth century Johann
Hieronymus Schröter spent virtually every clear night carefully drawing and measuring a large number of lunar craters.
Measuring the height of a mountain—or a ringwall—on the
moon is done by measuring the length of its shadow, noting,
of course, how many degrees of arc the sun was above the
horizon for that area at the time the shadow length was
measured. While engaged in calculating his results Schröter
noticed something that is still known as "Schröter's rule." It
says that the mass of the ringwall is roughly equivalent to the
volume of the depression which is the crater's floor. In other
words, if a ringwall were bulldozed into the depression it
surrounds, the hole would be filled in with very little lacking
or very little left over.

Schröter noted this fact with surprise; important conclu-
sions were drawn from it by others many decades later. The
work on lunar craters done by Schröter and his successors
led to what may be called a scheme of the topography of a
lunar crater. The craters were found to be virtually circular,
even though a large number of them, located near the limbs
of the moon, look elliptical because of foreshortening. Only a
very few actually elliptical craters are known. With one
conspicuous exception, the crater Wargentin, the floors are
below the level of the surrounding territory and generally flat,
except for smaller craters that may be located inside larger

craters and except for the central peak, which is a feature of about half of all larger craters. If a central peak is present it normally occupies the geometrical center of the ringwall. Drawings that can be found in older books showing a high and steep ringwall surrounding a deep circular gully that in turn surrounds a towering central peak almost looking like the towers of an old castle are quite impressive, but they have absolutely nothing to do with reality. The central peak does not quite reach the height of ground level outside the crater. As for the ringwall, the inside slope is always steeper than the outside slope.

Before going on to the next feature, the so-called "rays," a few words have to be said about the unusual formation named after the Swedish astronomer Per Wargentin. It is a circular formation in the southern part of the moon, lying, unfortunately, so near the limb that observation is quite difficult. The diameter of this formation is fifty-five miles and the crater floor is not a depression but is raised by about fourteen hundred feet. It looks as if a normal lunar crater has been filled up with some originally liquid or plastic substance that hardened later. In a small telescope the surface of this plateau looks flat; larger instruments show a fairly large number of hills and ridges.

The "rays" are white streaks which are very conspicuous when the sun is high over the areas of the moon where they are located. The moon's curvature makes them look curved if they are long enough, but it is easy to determine that they are straight in reality. They cross over *mare* plains, mountain ranges, and whatever else may be in their path with the greatest of ease and with astonishing impartiality. Some rays

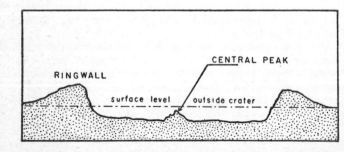

Fig. 14. Profile of a Lunar Crater. "Schröter's rule" is shown.

are hundreds of miles in length, and though they are not actually interrupted for any important distance, the long ones occasionally show weaker stretches, as if there were thin spots through which the darker background can be seen. Since they are strong when the sun is high over them but weak and nearly invisible when the sun is low, astronomers have watched for them especially right after sunrise and just prior to sunset (for the moon) with the purpose in mind to draw and measure their shadows.

The verdict came in at an early time: no ray was found to produce a shadow. Of course it was very likely that the shadows were too short to be seen in the earlier instruments. A fourteen-inch telescope was aspected to show something where a four-inch telescope had failed. But the result remained the same: no ray had ever been seen to cast a shadow. This of course proved that the material that formed the rays was only a thin layer on the background, maybe only a few yards in thickness, or only a few feet, or possibly just a few inches. But whatever the material was, it was associated with a crater.

Tycho is the one with the biggest, whitest, and most impressive ray system. But though the many individual streaks of this system come together at Tycho and certainly look as if they originated from this crater, there is a dark area surrounding the ringwall. None of the rays actually touches the crater; they originate a short distance away from it. The interior of the fifty-four-mile-diameter ringwall shows not a trace of the white material. The second largest ray system, less bright than that of Tycho, is associated with the crater Copernicus. The craters Kepler, Olbers, and Anaxagoras also have ray systems and a few far smaller craters are surrounded by bright patches with a few short extensions that might be taken to be rays that failed to develop, presumably for lack of material.

While the rays show no elevation that could be detected from earth and certainly are not depressions in the lunar surface, the features known as "rills" certainly are deep depressions. Schröter is usually credited with their discovery because he carefully drew them and also coined the term. But it is a fact that the Dutch physicist and astronomer Christiaan Huygens had seen and mentioned such a rill before Schröter. By this term, derived from the German word *Rille*, which means "groove," Schröter intended to indicate that they were both deep and straight. English-speaking astronomers referred to them as "rills," but during recent years the term "cleft" has come into usage, partly because large telescopes have shown that they are not as even as an artificial groove made for fitting pieces of furniture together.

The most typical of them is situated nicely in the center of the visible hemisphere of the moon and has a length of about one hundred miles. It originates near the small crater Ariadaeus, passes near but not through another small crater, named Silberschlag, and ends near the formation called Schneckenberg ("snail mountain," since it resembles the picture presented by a snail's shell that has been cut through), a little to the north of the beginning of another cleft, the Hyginus cleft. The latter is not straight like the Ariadaeus cleft, but decidedly curved. It is named after the crater Hyginus, which is in the middle of the sixty-mile cleft and also marks the point of its main bend. The Hyginus cleft runs roughly west to east and is quite straight until it arrives at Hyginus; from then on it continues in a northward-curving line. In small telescopes the Ariadaeus cleft and the Hyginus cleft looked very much alike, but better instruments showed a difference. The Ariadaeus cleft is still described as a straight crack in the moon, as it was described a hundred years ago. But the Hyginus cleft is for most of its length a chain of overlapping deep craterlets. One should not make any judgments at this moment in history, since first-hand-eyewitness reports are to be expected in about a decade, but what we

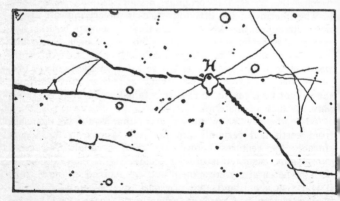

Fig. 15. The Hyginus Rill. The vicinity of the crater Hyginus (marked *H*), showing many small rills and a large number of craterlets. As can be seen, a part of the Hyginus rill is formed by a string of craterlets. The large rill entering the picture from the left is the end of the Ariadaeus rill.

know right now seems to indicate that the two formations are of different origin.

The crater Triesnecker, less than a hundred miles to the south of the end of the Hyginus cleft, has a whole system of clefts which are believed to be the result of collapses; their walls are less steep than those of the others and they also seem to be less deep. The widths of the Triesnecker clefts are around three miles and their depths are estimated to be on the order of one mile. A formation originating in the crater Herodotus, located next to the now famous crater Aristarchus (see next chapter), goes under the name of Herodotus rill in older books. But it is not a typical rill, or cleft, in many respects—it comes out of Herodotus, widens in places, describes a horseshoe curve, and is not very deep. Hence it is now known as "Schröter's valley," but what forces on a waterless world could form such a valley is as much a mystery as is the origin of the Ariadaeus cleft.

The next feature to be discussed is the "domes," so named because they look somewhat like the carapace of a large turtle, though I am tempted to say that they look like the concrete "Block Houses" of the Atlas launch complex at Cape Kennedy. They are a fairly recent discovery; the first to be described was noticed in 1932 by the British astronomer Robert Barker inside the crater Darwin. Barker called it "a huge cinder heap." The American astronomer S. R. B. Cooke found several other domes, and another American, Professor Gerard P. Kuiper, announced the discovery of a dozen domes in 1959. Kuiper, probably mainly influenced by the fact that many domes display a small dark hole near their centers, expressed the opinion that the domes were "extinct volcanoes."

In the meantime two British observers, P. J. Cattermole and Patrick Moore, had also looked for domes systematically, mainly using Moore's 12½-inch reflector telescope, which, as Moore wrote later, "showed that domes existed not in ones or twos, but in dozens." Their catalog listed over seventy of them in 1961, including the ones found by Kuiper (the two British observers and Kuiper worked completely independently), but they are convinced that there are many more since "domes in rough areas are unpleasantly hard to detect."

"Several interesting facts emerged," Moore wrote in his *Survey of the Moon;* "first, the domes are not spread about at random, but occur in clusters. For instance, there are eight inside the crater Capuanus ... while other rich areas lie near Arago on the *Mare tranquillitatis,* near Prinz in the Harbin-

ger Mountains and on various parts of the *Oceanus procellarum*. There is, for instance, a superb example of a dome near
the little crater Milichius. Secondly, many of the domes proved
to have summit pits, giving them a striking resemblance to
true volcanoes. Some of the pits were clear enough to be seen
even in a 6-inch telescope, and can be photographed,
though most of them were much more delicate. It seems,
indeed, that summit pits are the rule and not the exception."

Craters, rays, rills or clefts, and domes do not yet exhaust
the list of lunar features. There are a few more, faults like
earthquake faults on earth, ridges which also resemble terrestrial mountain ridges, so-called ghost ridges (and ghost
craters), and finally large mountains.

Faults are numerous but it would not serve any useful
purpose to enumerate them in this book. Only the most
famous one, located in the *Mare nubium,* shall be mentioned.
It is known as the Straight Wall (and has even been nick-
named the Railroad) but it is not perfectly straight and it is
not a wall-like formation. It is a quite normal fault, though
its length of sixty miles is spectacular. An observer can see it
either as a dark or as a light line, both effects caused by the
sun's position over the *Mare nubium.* The fact is simply that
the plain on one side of the fault is about a thousand feet
higher than on the other side. The rising sun shines from the
direction of the higher side, so that the fault casts a shadow
which shows up as an almost straight black line. When the
sun is high above the fault it becomes invisible; then, during
the lunar afternoon it begins to show as a bright line, because
the slanting rays of the sun illuminate its inclined side. There
has been a fair amount of debate of how the Straight Wall
would look to an astronaut standing on the lower portion of
the plain. Originally it was thought to be vertical, or nearly
so, but the American astronomer John Ashbrook, after going
over the drawings and photographs of the shadow, came to
the conclusion that the angle is not steeper than forty-five
degrees of arc, and it may even be less.

The ghost ridges and ghost craters are well named, which
is evident when you know what the name is supposed to
indicate. They are mere outlines of ridges and craters and
look as if a regular ridge of hills or a regular crater had been
subjected to a prolonged bombardment with concentrated
heat rays until the rock melted down, leaving only a trace of
its former existence. An astronaut on the spot would probably see softly rounded shoulders of low height, but the

experts have braced themselves in advance against any surprises which such future reports are likely to contain.

The great mountain chains like the ones surrounding the *Mare imbrium* will probably look like the Alps or the Rocky Mountains to an exploring astronaut, except that no mountain will be snowcapped and no valley filled by a glacier. Our moon may not be completely without water, but it is certain that there is no water in any form visible at its surface. Because of the absence of snow and ice in the lunar mountains, artists who tried to picture a lunar landscape always showed the mountains as jagged rocks not softened by erosion. True, the kind of erosion with which we are familiar on earth does not exist on the moon, but there are other forces which can soften the outlines of a rock formation, and many lunar observers of our time feel that the older idea of sharp spires may be wrong.

But it is impossible to speak about lunar mountain chains without mentioning the biggest—in every meaning of the word—puzzle on the visible hemisphere of the moon. It is the Great Valley of the lunar Alps (Fig. 16), which simply has no counterpart on earth.

The first thought that occurs to almost anybody who sees the Great Valley through a telescope is that it must have

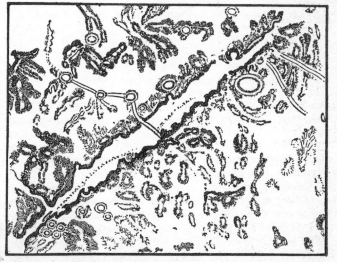

Fig. 16. The Great Valley of the Alps. Drawn at the turn of the century by Philipp Fauth.

been gouged out by an enormous meteorite traveling parallel
to the moon's surface. Detailed examination of the valley fails
to agree completely with this first impression; at the very least
one would have to assume that a number of smaller changes
took place later. The alternative to the hypothesis of a
glancing collision is that the valley is the result of a subsi-
dence in a faulted zone. That explanation, at least to my
mind, is no explanation at all. But no decision is possible
until an investigation on the spot has taken place; investigation from a distance will never solve the riddle of the Great
Valley of the lunar Alps.

Let us turn now from such specialized puzzles to more
general questions, beginning with the moon's atmosphere.

A few years ago, after a lecture to students of the University of Texas, I walked across the campus with some of these
students. It was quite cold and the night was clear, with a
nearly full moon overhead. We stopped for a moment to
look up and one of the girl students exclaimed: "It is so clear
you can actually *see* that there is no atmosphere on the
moon!" Since she had an atmosphere in mind that would be
dense enough to breathe in and that could support clouds,
she was perfectly correct. But if the term atmosphere is used
to describe a veil of gas around the body of the moon, the
question is by no means simple.

Some of the earlier observers of the moon, for example, Sir
William Herschel and the indefatigable Johann Hieronymus
Schröter, had assumed the existence of a lunar atmosphere,
presumably without thinking very hard about it. It may be
presumed that they were not acquainted with a book by a
Jesuit astronomer, Father Roger Boscovitch, or else one
would expect them to have said why they did not agree with
him. Father Boscovitch, who was born in what is now
Yugoslavia, wrote a book with the title *De Lunae Atmos-
phaera* ("On the Moon's Atmosphere"), which was first
published in Rome in 1753. His method of presenting his
case was to assume that the moon did have an atmosphere,
to reason out the results to be expected from the presence of
an atmosphere, and then to compare these results with actual
observations. If the moon had an atmosphere, for example,
the phases of the moon would differ slightly from the predicted phases and the shadows of mountains would not be as
sharp as they are. But the moon's atmosphere would betray
its existence most definitely on the occasion of an "occultation."
This term means that the disk of the moon covers the
image of a star or of a planet. As the moon slowly closes

in on a planet (compared to the fast motion of the moon, the planet can be considered motionless) the light from the planet would first reach us by shining through the moon's atmosphere before it is blotted out by the body of the moon. This would have several effects: first, the light of the planet would be dimmed gradually prior to its disappearance; second, the light of the planet would be bent in the moon's atmosphere so that we would still see the planet for a short time when it is actually already behind the moon; third, since blue light is bent more strongly than red light, the planet would look bicolored for a moment or two, acquiring a red edge on the side nearer to the moon and a blue edge on the other side. None of this could be observed; hence it had to be concluded that the moon's atmosphere, if it had one at all, had to be far less dense than that of the earth. Early in this century an astronomer who had, naturally, far better instruments at his disposal than Father Boscovitch tried to establish just how dense, or rather how thin, the lunar atmosphere had to be to escape observation. He concluded that if the moon's atmosphere at the lunar surface had a density of 1/200 of the density of our atmosphere at sea level he could still have detected its presence. Since he had failed to find it the density had to be below this value. A repetition of these measurements with the instruments now available would probably lead to the result that even a density of 1/20,000 would still be discovered.

But the question is whether there is a veil of gases at all, no matter how attenuated. That question must be answered with "yes." The moon must have its share of naturally radioactive elements, and these elements, in decaying, release gases. The gases produced are the kind collectively known as the "rare," or "noble," gases, listed in the following table.

NAME AND CHEMICAL SYMBOL		MEANING	ATOMIC WEIGHT
Helium	(He)	sun	4.0
Neon	(Ne)	new	20.2
Argon	(A)	inert	39.9
Krypton	(Kr)	hidden	83.7
Xenon	(Xe)	stranger	131.3
Radon*	(Rn)	——	222.0

* Radon was originally named niton (shining), but the name was later changed to indicate its close relationship to radium.

While there can be no doubt that these gases are produced steadily, it is impossible to arrive at any reasonably correct conclusion as to the density of the moon's veil of noble gases. We don't know yet whether the percentage of naturally radioactive elements in the moon's crust is the same as on earth. It is not likely to be much higher, but it may be far less. Strangely enough, we can be more positive about the composition of the lunar gas veil, because we know which gases the moon can hold.

The ability of a body of planetary mass to hold on to an atmosphere depends on two factors. One is very simply its size, or rather its mass. A more massive body can hold a bigger atmosphere than a lesser body. But the other important factor is the temperature that prevails inside such an atmosphere. The molecules (or atoms) of a gas move faster the higher the temperature. If the molecules of a gas move with a higher velocity than the planet's escape velocity (1.5 miles per second in the case of the moon), this particular gas will slowly but surely escape from the planet and be dissipated in space. Logically a planet orbiting the sun at a very great distance will be able to retain gases which another planet of the same mass but orbiting closer to the sun could not hold.

The highest temperature to be expected on the moon—at the equator, sometime after noon for a given area—is estimated to be 135 degrees Centigrade, or 275 degrees Fahrenheit. At that temperature the velocity of all molecules (or atoms) of a weight of less than sixty will be greater than the escape velocity. All the gases which form the bulk of the earth's atmosphere would therefore escape from the moon, for an oxygen molecule (O_2) has a weight of thirty-two, a nitrogen molecule (N_2) has a weight of twenty-eight, a molecule of water vapor (H_2O) has a weight of only eighteen and a molecule of carbon dioxide (CO_2) has a weight of forty-four. Considering the noble gases produced by radioactive decay, only krypton and xenon would stay near the moon's surface.[1] If we assume that there is still some residual volcanic activity on the moon there would be an additional source for the production of gases. Volcanoes produce mainly water vapor and carbon dioxide, both of which are too light to be held, but sulfur dioxide (SO_2), which is also produced by volcanic

[1] Radon is radioactive itself, with a half-life of only 3.85 days, so that it, if formed, disappears for other reasons, producing the very light helium in the process.

eruptions, has a molecular weight of sixty-four and is heavy enough to be retained.

Argon, the result of radioactive decay, is a borderline case. Its most common isotope has a weight of forty and is therefore too light to be retained indefinitely. But it is just heavy enough to slow down its rate of dissipation; therefore the presence of argon would depend mainly on its production rate, which we don't know.

Our moon, then, must be surrounded by a thin veil of gas consisting mainly of xenon, with an admixture of krypton and possibly argon with traces of sulfur dioxide.

As we have seen, the existence of an atmosphere depends on the temperature, which on the moon is a very variable factor indeed. The statement that can be read in so many places that the nighttime temperature of the moon is *minus* 240 degrees Fahrenheit, while the daytime temperature is 275 degrees Fahrenheit, is not actually wrong, but it applies only to the lunar equator. Elsewhere on the moon the nights are just as cold, but the daytime temperatures are not as high. In the area of *Sinus iridum,* the great "bay" of the *Mare imbrium,* the temperature of the surface does not rise beyond fifty to fifty-five degrees Fahrenheit during the day. The coming lunar base will be established well away from the lunar equator for this reason, though the first landing on the moon will have to be near the equator for reasons that will be explained later.

And now we come to the problem of dust on the moon. That the moon must have a surface layer of dust is accepted by all astronomers. But there is a wide divergence of opinion about the thickness of the dust layer. The English astronomer Thomas Gold suggested at one time that the smoothness of the large *mare* plains is due to the fact that they are enormous dust bowls where all surface irregularities are smoothed out by the dust. Others consider the *mare* to be old lava flows, now frozen and hard and covered by a dust layer about an inch thick, with a maximum thickness of about a foot in some places.

The moon's dust layer is a problem that shows a remarkable similarity to the problem of the lunar atmosphere, where we could say that there must be some gases and could even say what gases and why but could say nothing about the quantity. In the case of the dust layer we cannot arrive at a conclusion as to its thickness, but we can say that dust must be present and why.

Lunar dust has three sources. A certain percentage of it will literally be space dust, tiny meteorites much smaller than a grain of sand that have accumulated over millions of years. Another portion of the lunar dust is also due to meteorites, but larger ones that pounded some of the lunar surface into dust when they struck, being shattered themselves in the process. The third dust-producing factor is the cosmic rays that strike the moon's surface. Cosmic rays are not "rays" in the customary meaning of that word; they are subatomic particles moving at high velocities. The majority of them are protons, nuclei of hydrogen atoms, coming from the sun, but some cosmic rays are alpha particles, nuclei of helium atoms, weighing four times as much as the protons. When subatomic particles like these strike rocks they break down the crystal structure of the molecules forming the rocks, with the result that the rock crumbles into dust.

Of course the dust that has been formed in the past will protect the rock below, and there have naturally been attempts to calculate how much of a dust layer would be needed to shield the underlying rock from additional cosmic-ray damage. Of course different particles have different energies, depending on their velocities, but for protons coming from the sun it could be calculated that an eight-inch dust layer would protect the material below. In other words, if lunar dust were formed only by protons coming from the sun, the thickness of the dust layer could not be above eight inches. Of course the flanks of a mountain would stay unprotected since all the dust produced would drop off, exposing new and undamaged rock, while the dust would accumulate at the foot of the mountain. If this reasoning is correct, the deepest dust drifts should be found at the base of steep cliffs.

But whether the average thickness of the dust cover is five feet or a quarter of an inch, it poses a few problems. Our moon, no matter how bright and silvery it might look in the night sky, is a fairly dark body, for it reflects only seven percent of the light it receives from the sun.

That is somewhat surprising all by itself; combined with the fact of a dust cover consisting of rock that has been pounded into powder, it turns into a startling fact. If you take rock samples of various kinds and pound them into powder with a hammer, you will almost always get a powder that is much lighter in color than the original rock. Just to make things a little more surprising, it has been shown by laboratory experiments that proton bombardment also lightens the color of rocks. Two French astronomers, A. Dollfuss and Bernard Lyot, set out to find a material that would be dark enough to reflect light the way the moon does, even when ground into powder. Dollfuss first established by theoretical reasoning that the material in question would have to be dark in color, opaque, and of small-particle size but that even these small particles still had to have a rough surface. Then Lyot found such material: it was finely ground volcanic ash.

This discovery, of course, went well with the idea that the *mare* were hardened lava flows. After they had hardened they had been pounded for millions of years by impacts of meteorites of all sizes. At first the rubble may have been rough, but additional pounding ground the rubble into dust and the result is the peculiar way the moon reflects light.

But while investigating the reflectivity of terrestrial materials and comparing it with the way the moon reflects sunlight, another riddle turned up. The moon showed a surprising amount of what is called "backscatter." The amount of light reflected from most materials remains substantially the same whether the light strikes the material vertically (with the observer behind the light source) or at an angle. A strong change in reflectivity if the light is reflected straight back is what is called backscatter. The moon showed much more backscatter than had been expected.

We can produce backscatter artificially. Some highway signs take advantage of this optical phenomenon so that they stand out sharply in the dark when hit by the beams from the headlights of a car. The method is simple: the highway sign is covered with a layer of glass beads. But we cannot expect that to be the explanation for the moon's backscatter; besides, the other characteristics of lunar reflectivity would be changed. However, backscatter can be produced by the proper shape of the material that reflects the light. The shape has to be such that it hides its own shadows, and the most common example of such a shape is a tree.

If you fly over a forest going north at noon, when the sun is high in the south, the boughs of the trees will hide their own shadows from your view and the forest will look uncommonly bright. But if the pilot then executes a turn, you'll see both illuminated treetops and the shadows they cast, and the picture will be less bright quite suddenly. While trees are the most common shape on earth that will produce backscatter, their size has nothing to do with it. A large stand of mushrooms would produce the same effect and a large number of thumbtacks stuck in a piece of cardboard will do it too. As regards the moon, it was therefore necessary to conceive of something producing backscatter. It only needed to have the proper shape and had to be something likely to occur on the moon; its size was unimportant.

The American astronomer Bruce Hapke succeeded in combining the backscatter requirement with the fact that there is a dust layer on the moon. Hapke dribbled very fine cement dust through a fine sieve and watched what happened. Well, what happened was that a cement-dust particle would adhere to other dust particles at the point of first contact. It would not fall off and fill available space between the other particles. The dust particles built up tiny structures that when seen through a powerful magnifying glass showed some resemblance to coral reefs. Here was a shape which was both possible on the moon and which would produce backscatter by hiding its own shadows when seen from above. The actual height of these structures could be less than one eighth of an inch; they did not need to be large to produce the observed effect.

Hapke coined the name "fairy castles" for such tiny dust structures. They would form when a tiny meteorite made an impact in the dust, throwing up a small dust cloud. The particles, settling back slowly under the light pull of the lunar gravity, would build up fairy castles which, on the windless

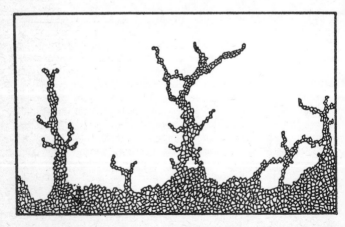

Fig. 17. Fairy Castles. Fragile dust structures believed to cover the surface of the moon and to cause the observed backscatter. Their height is probably less than one tenth of an inch.

moon, would last indefinitely, or until another meteorite impacted in the vicinity, throwing up another dust cloud that would build new ones.

The actual lunar surface, then, must consist of bedrock covered by a dust layer of unknown thickness, which in turn is covered by a very thin layer of fluffy fairy castles.

4. The Mystery of the Red Spots

Karl von Linné, a famous Swedish botanist and originator of the system of classification of plants and animals, died in 1778. His life and work were well removed from astronomy, but he gets into the story because sometime after his death a crater on the moon was named for him. In English-speaking countries Linné is better known by the Latinized version of his name, Carolus Linnaeus. But in Europe he is known as Linné, the name entered in the birth register of the village of Råshult, in the province of Småland, presumably by his own father, who was the village pastor. Since the lunar crater was named by a European, the name became Linné, not Linnaeus.

The crater Linné is located in the *Mare serenitatis*, not far from the center of the lunar disk, and it is quite isolated, with no surface features nearby other than a few low ridges. Wilhelm Gotthelf Lohrmann entered it in Section IV of his *Lunar Map in Twenty-five Sections,* the first four sections of which were published in 1824. Linné is not yet named on this map, but referred to as crater A; in his explanatory text Lohrmann wrote that crater A appeared to be *mehr als eine Meile im Durchmesser*. This translates as "more than one mile in diameter," but it must be remembered that Lohrmann used the then customary German mile, which was the equivalent of 4.5 statute miles. At any event crater A must have been clearly visible. Soon after Lohrmann, J. H. von Mädler in Berlin drew the crater too—on his map, published in 1837, the name Linné is used—and assigned a diameter of 1.4 (German) miles to it. He also remarked that it seemed to be very deep. Finally Julius Schmidt made several drawings of the crater during the years from 1841 to 1843.

It was the same Julius Schmidt who in 1866 announced

that the crater Linné had disappeared and that a white patch had taken its place, about six (English) miles in diameter. This announcement was quickly followed by another one: he had seen a small mountain in the center of the white spot. One month after that Father Angelo Secchi announced from Rome that the small mountain was really a craterlet about half a mile in diameter. And a short time later Heinrich Ludwig d'Arrest reported that the 10.5-inch instrument at Copenhagen had enabled him to determine the true diameter of the craterlet as being 1.5 miles.

The conclusion drawn from this succession of reports by many astronomers of the period was that Linné, when it had been observed by Lohrmann and Von Mädler, had been a dead volcanic crater. It evidently had come to life again sometime between 1843 and 1866 and covered the area with a layer of volcanic ash. The craterlet first seen by Father Secchi probably was the new crater. One could hope for further volcanic activity and one could even hope that an observer might see another eruption take place.

These hopes remained unfulfilled. Linné is still a white patch about six miles in diameter, still easy to find because of its isolation.

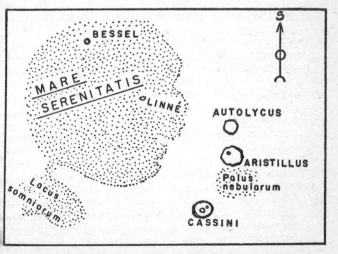

Fig. 18. Map Sketch of the Location of Linné. Unlike the *Mare imbrium* (see Fig. 3), the *Mare serenitatis* shows only two interruptions; one is the crater Bessel and the other the much-discussed white patch called Linné.

Gradually doubts that a change had actually taken place began to creep into astronomical literature, some of them bearing the hallmark of quibbling. Julius Schmidt, when he made his early drawings, had been a teen-age boy and inexperienced. Of course Von Mädler had been an excellent observer, but his instrument had been quite small, only a 3¾-inch refracting telescope. Lohrmann had, after all, been an amateur astronomer. More serious (for those who believed that an actual change had taken place) was the discovery of a white patch in the *Mare serenitatis* on the maps made by Schröter. But it could be pointed out that this white patch was not quite in the right position to be Linné and that Schröter had also charted a dark spot which might be Linné as easily as the white spot.

The debate has been continuing, on and off, in this manner to the present day. One party insists that it is highly improbable that Lohrmann and Von Mädler both made the same mistake, especially since Linné is not a part of a jumble of other craters but splendidly alone. The other party says that anybody can make a mistake, that Linné looks different depending on the height of the sun over the *Mare serenitatis* and that Schröter drew a white patch. It is conveniently overlooked in this connection that Schröter was "an amateur" too. He was a public servant, and Lohrmann was a surveyor.

The case is not proved in either direction, and part of the difficulty lies in the fact that all the maps were hand-drawn. If one wants to be careful, no fine detail on any hand-drawn chart can be cited as an absolute proof. Observers do get tired, or they may hurry because a cloud bank is closing in. They may put in some detail from memory, or they may neglect some detail because their attention is focused on something else. I am not trying to blacken the reputation of the excellent lunar observers of the past; I am trying to point out that a photographic plate cannot neglect any detail, whereas an observer drawing charts can do so. If somebody, for example, spotted a small crater on a photograph which an older observer should have seen (considering the power of his telescope) but did not draw, it would not prove that this crater was then missing. It would prove only that so-and-so did not draw it.

The reason why I bring up small craters missing on older charts but present on all modern photographs is a letter which I received a few years ago. It read about as follows (I am quoting from memory): "... if it is true that most of the

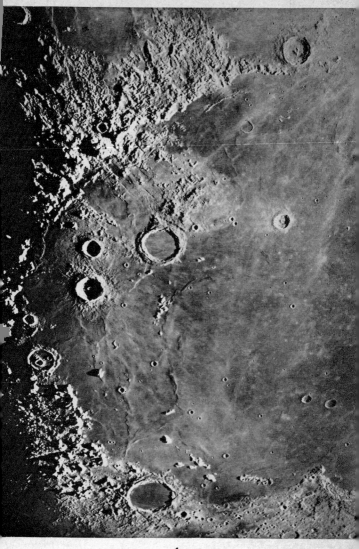

1

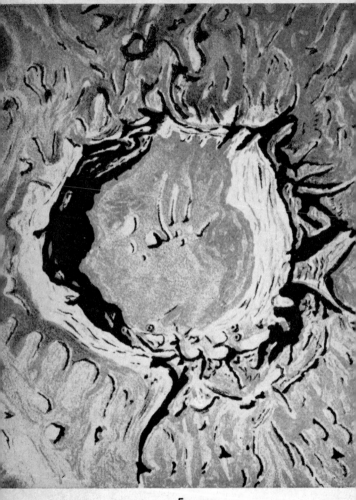

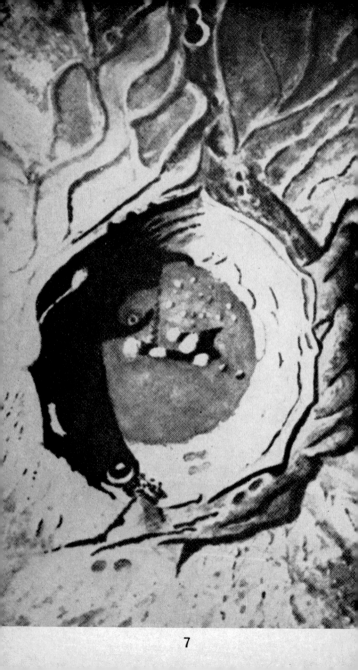

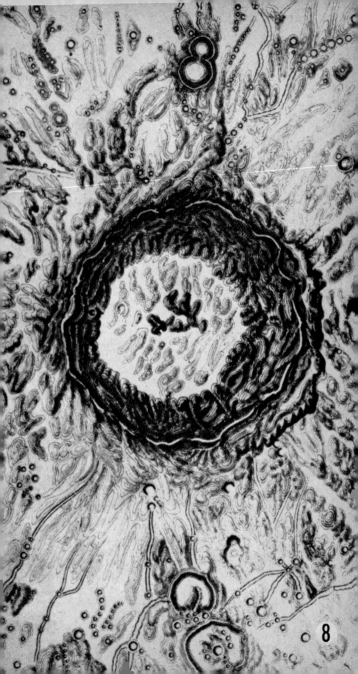

8

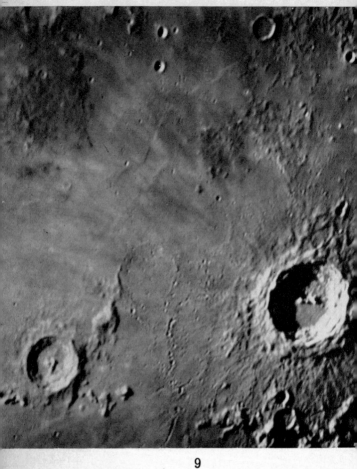

9

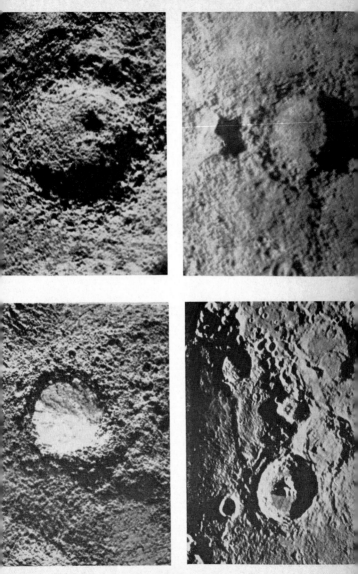

13

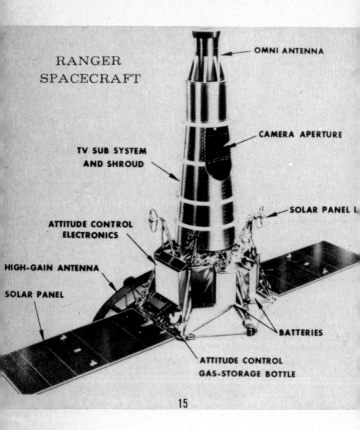

14

RANGER
SPACECRAFT

OMNI ANTENNA

CAMERA APERTURE

TV SUB SYSTEM
AND SHROUD

SOLAR PANEL L

ATTITUDE CONTROL
ELECTRONICS

HIGH-GAIN ANTENNA

SOLAR PANEL

BATTERIES

ATTITUDE CONTROL
GAS-STORAGE BOTTLE

15

16

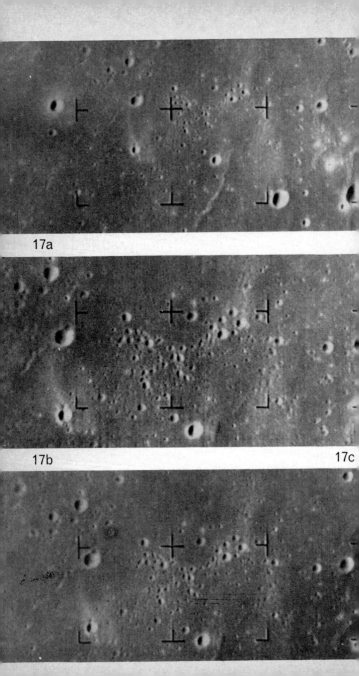

17a

17b

17c

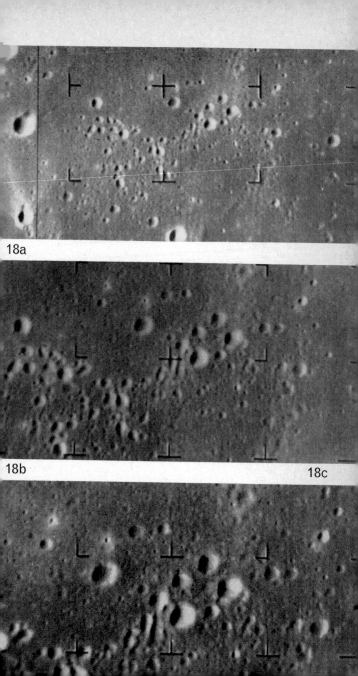

18a

18b   18c

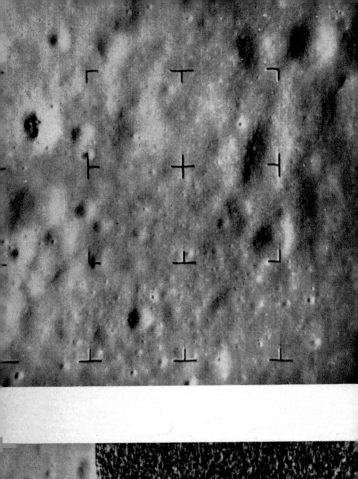

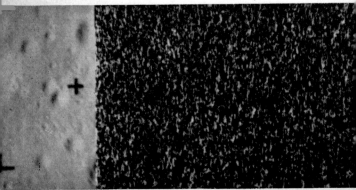

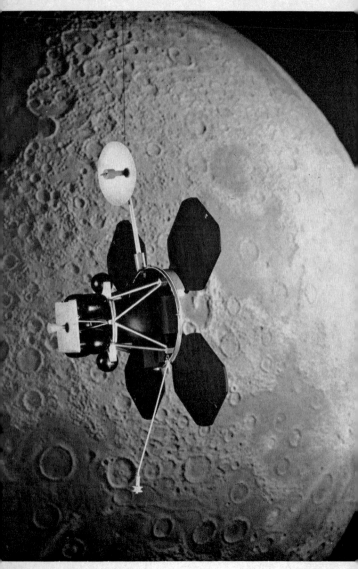

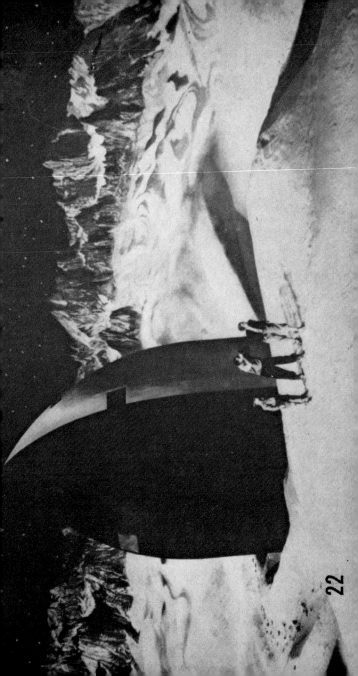
22

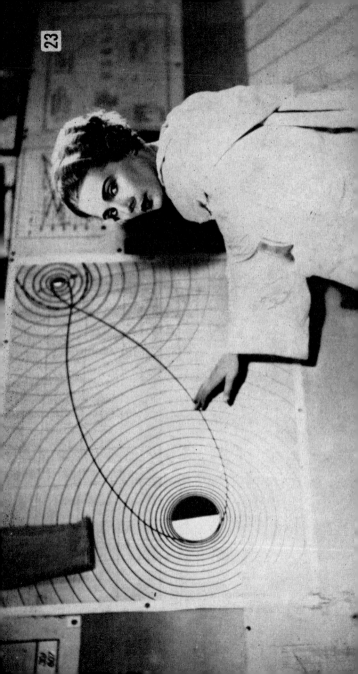

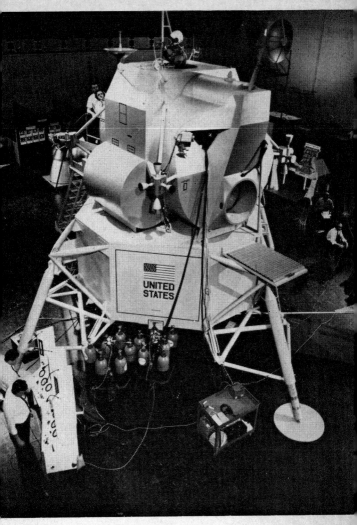

lunar craters were caused by the impact of meteorites, why has no new crater been formed during the last century, during which the moon has been under careful observation? As you know, the earth has been hit twice by very large meteorites since the beginning of the current century, first in 1908 and then again in 1947. The moon should have sustained at least one hit since the beginning of careful observation."

Considering what has been said about the possible short-comings of hand-drawn charts, any discussion about the appearance of new craters has to be limited to the "photographic period," a little more than a century. Now, it is true that the earth was struck twice by large bodies, in 1908 and in 1947. The impacts both happened to take place in eastern Siberia. The earlier one struck near a river named Podkamennaya Tunguska and is now believed to have been a small comet. The later impact was in the Sikhote-Alin mountains to the north of Vladivostok; this one is known to have been a mass of iron that fragmented before impact and may even have been a cloud of fragments before it entered the atmosphere.

Of course all meteorite impacts are random events; we cannot, from the fact that two struck the earth within half a century, derive a rule that there have been or will be four major impacts per century. But let us, for the sake of discussion, accept such a rule temporarily. The point here is that the earth is a much larger target than the moon; if both bodies are considered as round targets in space, the earth is a target of about fourteen times the area of the lunar target. Therefore, if the earth sustained four hits per century, it would take three and a half centuries until the earth had accumulated fourteen hits. In that period of time, if everything went according to such rules, the moon would collect one impact. But the probability that this one impact took place on the far side of the moon is equal to the probability of impact on the visible hemisphere. Therefore the fact that no new lunar crater has been formed since 1900 is by no means surprising. Of course it may happen while I am writing this; it might happen tomorrow or next month. But the probability that it will is very small.

Since I received that letter four impacts on the moon have taken place: the Russian payload of eight hundred and sixty pounds in 1959 and three Ranger payloads of about eight hundred pounds each in January and July, 1964, and in February, 1965. Even the somewhat heavier Russian probe was not heavy enough to produce a crater that can be seen or photographed from earth. Presumably a meteorite that could cause a crater visible to us would have to weigh well over one ton.

Let us return to the debate about changes on the moon. Certainly the discovery of a lunar feature on a photograph that cannot be found on older charts is no proof that it was formed in the meantime. One is on somewhat firmer ground if the early observers did draw the feature in question, but drew and described it differently from what we see now. But as the debate about Linné has shown, even in such a case there is no unanimity of opinion. The same applies to reported possible changes elsewhere on the moon, for example, the interior of the large and conspicuous crater Plato.

Every astronomer knew that a really good case could be made in only two ways. One would be that a photograph taken in 1964 differs from one taken in 1924, *provided* that both photographs were taken while the sun was at the same height over the lunar formation and the change could not be explained away by a difference in libration. The other would be that an observer could say that he had actually seen the change while it took place. In the latter case there could be no doubt, or so it seemed.

One such report that attracted much attention—to a large degree because it came from a very eminent astronomer—was the one published by William H. Pickering in 1924. Pickering had assumed for some time that small darkish patches that changed color in the course of the lunar day indicated vegetation. But in the crater Eratosthenes he found dark patches that seemed to move slowly, at the rate of a few feet per minute. He thought them to be insects, comparable to swarms of locusts, which moved from their breeding places to patches of vegetation. Naturally other astronomers began to watch the spots in Eratosthenes, but nobody agreed wholeheartedly with Pickering. The most recent statement about the patches in Eratosthenes which I have been able to find was written by Patrick Moore and can be found in his book *Survey of the Moon*. He wrote: "My own studies of them, carried out between 1954 and the present time [1963], indicate that although the patches exist, they do not move. Certain parts of the crater floor brighten under a high sun, while others become less obvious; but this is a very different matter from a patch in actual motion. I have never seen the slightest sign of anything of the sort, even though I have made hundreds of drawings of the area under every conceivable angle of illumination. The same is true of rather similar patches reported by Pickering inside the crater Aristillus. . . ."

While Pickering was obviously deceived by the appearance of fine detail near the limit of visibility, other observers reported something that could not be explained away. The British astronomer H. Percy Wilkins pointed out in 1954 that sometimes well-known small features in well-known large craters were *not* visible, but could be seen again on a later occasion. This can be explained in one way only: something must have covered up the small features. If the moon were the earth, one would say that this detail was obscured by fog and haze, but most astronomers would have said immediately that they could not imagine where a haze on the moon could come from and that they were at a loss even to guess what kind of a haze it could be. But then Dinsmore Alter of Los Angeles, on October 26, 1956, succeeded in photographing such an obscuration in the crater Alphonsus. Nobody could doubt anymore that it did happen, though an explanation was still lacking.

Alphonsus is one of the craters with a central peak, and during the night from November 3 to November 4, 1958, the Russian astronomer Nikolai A. Kozyrev of the Astrophysical Observatory in the Crimea saw an unusual event in or on the central peak of Alphonsus.

During October and November, 1958, Kozyrev and V. I. Ezerski of the Kharkov Observatory were mainly engaged in taking spectrograms of the planet Mars, using the fifty-inch reflector of the Crimean Observatory. But because of Dinsmore Alter's photographic proof of an obscuration in Alphonsus, Kozyrev took spectrograms of the moon and especially of Alphonsus whenever possible.

"Nothing special," Kozyrev wrote afterwards, "was noticed on the spectrograms of Alphonsus up to the night of November 2-3, when three spectrograms were taken. . . . While I was taking the first spectrogram at 1^h Universal Time [8:00 p.m., Eastern Standard Time] and guiding [the instrument] on the image of the central peak, the latter became strongly washed out and of an unusual reddish hue. After taking this spectrogram, however, and in accordance with our program, we changed over to observe Mars, and the next spectrogram of Alphonsus was made from 3:00 to 3:30 Universal Time [10:00-10:30 p.m. E.S.T.], a 30-minute exposure. Only the central peak of this crater showed on the slit, and I was struck by the unusual brightness and whiteness at the time.

During the exposure I did not take my eye away from the guiding eyepiece, but suddenly I noticed that the brightness of the peak had fallen to its normal value. ... On the following night I obtained two more spectra of Alphonsus, but its condition continued to be normal. Then the moon entered the last quarter phase and this region of its surface was in shadow and unobservable."

Dr. Kozyrev thought at first that the observed changes in brightness were caused by "a change in the quality of the observing conditions"; in other words, he regarded them as being due to changes in our own atmosphere. But his spectrograms told him that for the duration of at least thirty minutes, the duration of the exposure, there had been a gas cloud containing carbon. It is, of course, likely that the gas cloud was already there while the instrument was still aimed at Mars during the two hours between the first and the second spectrogram. Kozyrev concluded that he had witnessed a sign of volcanic activity, beginning with an ejection of dust and followed by an ejection of gas containing carbon dioxide. "The effusion of gas," he wrote, "could come from magma rising to the lunar surface."

British selenographers advanced a somewhat different interpretation: instead of magma rising to the surface, a volcanic eruption which did not fully develop, it could have been just a sudden release of carbon dioxide gas, carrying surface dust with it and thereby "washing out" the central peak. But two things were clear: an astronomer, using a powerful instrument, had actually witnessed a change taking place, but it had not been one that actually changed the topography of the area. Pictures taken by American observers as soon as that area of the moon was again illuminated by the sun did not differ at all from pictures taken on earlier occasions.

In a way this was more interesting than witnessing a meteorite impact, because impacts, even if rare, were expected, but activity of any kind in the lunar crust without an outside cause had not been expected.

The next surprise came five years later, this time from two American observers, Dr. James A. Greenacre and Dr. Edward Barr, engaged in the lunar-mapping program of the U.S. Air Force. They began their work, which they expected to be routine, in the evening of October 29, 1963, using the twenty-four-inch refracting telescope of the Lowell Observatory. Observations were visual, not photographic. The area under observation was the crater Aristarchus and the neighboring crater Herodotus, from which Schröter's Valley extends northward.

The sun was nearly sixty degrees high over this area of the moon, so shadows were quite short. Suddenly Dr. Greenacre noticed an orange-red spot on one side of Schröter's Valley and immediately afterward another spot of the same color on a hilltop across the valley. Within two minutes the spots became quite bright and began to sparkle. Greenacre immediately called his colleague to share the observation. After Barr had confirmed the existence of the spots, Greenacre removed the deep-yellow filter that had been used for the expected routine observations so that they could judge the color better. Without the filter, both agreed, the two spots looked reddish-orange.

About five minutes after the appearance of the two spots

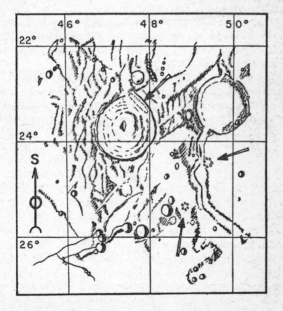

Fig. 19. The Red Spots on the Moon. The area of Aristarchus (the crater with the central peak) and Herodotus, from which Schröter's Valley extends toward the bottom of the picture. The three red spots, marked by arrows, appeared on the inside of the rim of Aristarchus and to both sides of the valley.

on both sides of Schröter's Valley, a long pink streak appeared on the inside of the rim of Aristarchus.

"No other hue," wrote Dr. Greenacre in *Sky and Telescope,* "could be seen on the inside or outside of this crater. Again, Mr. Barr and I observed with and without the filter; the only difference seemed to be a somewhat brighter color in unfiltered light. The colored area along the rim of Aristarchus did not sparkle like the other two spots. The eyepiece field of view was large enough to have all three areas in sight at the same time. At approximately 7:00 p.m. I noticed that the spots at the Cobra Head [the name of a widening of Schröter's Valley] and on the hill across the valley had changed to a light ruby red, yet their density and sparkle were still sufficient to hide the surface underneath. I had the impression that I was looking into a large polished gem ruby but could not see through it.... By 7:05 it was apparent that the color was fading."

The two red patches near Schröter's Valley disappeared first, having lasted about twenty minutes. The pink streak on Aristarchus, which had come into existence a little later, also disappeared last, also having lasted for about twenty minutes. After the spots had been entered on a chart, their size could be estimated. The one near the Cobra Head had been elliptical, measuring 5 by 1.5 miles; the one on the hilltop across the valley was smaller, with a diameter of about 1.5 miles; the pink streak on the inside of the ringwall of Aristarchus had displayed a width of about 1.5 miles and had been 11 miles long.

On November 27, 1963, the rim of Aristarchus again glowed red; this time the streak was about twelve miles long (with the same width as before) and lasted for 1¾ hours. It was seen by four men at the Lowell Observatory, including Dr. John S. Hall, the observatory's director. While others observed, Dr. Hall telephoned the Perkins Observatory of Ohio State University, which is not far from the Lowell Observatory but has a sixty-nine-inch reflecting telescope. The observer using it, graduate student Peter A. Boyce, was told only that something was going on in the region of Aristarchus. Boyce saw the red marking immediately and reported a location that agreed almost exactly with the location as seen by the men at the Lowell Observatory. There the activity had changed from observation to picture-taking, using seventy-millimeter black-and-white film. But the pictures showed nothing unusual; there were no changes that would show in black and white; it was apparently just a change in color.

The first reaction in professional circles was, naturally, surprise, and hard on the heels of the surprise there followed an apologetic attitude, the apologies being directed at a long-dead great astronomer, Sir William Herschel. On May 4, 1783, Sir William had written a letter to a J. H. de Magellan, a Portuguese scientist living in London. Part of the letter read: "I perceived in the dark part of the moon a luminous spot. It had the appearance of a red star of about the 4th magnitude. It was situated in the place of *Hevelii Mons Porphyrites*, the instrument with which I saw it was a 10 feet Newtonian Reflector of 9 inches aperture. Dr. Lind's lady who looked in the telescope immediately saw it, tho' no person had mentioned it, and compared it to a star. Dr. Lind tried to see it in an achromatic 3½ feet of Dollond's but could not perceive it, tho' he easily saw it in my reflector. . . ."

In April, 1787, Herschel saw luminous points again and this time he made a formal report to the Royal Society, saying that on April 19, 1787: "I perceive three volcanoes in different places of the dark part of the new moon. Two of them are either already extinct, or otherwise in a state of going to break out. . . . The third shows an actual eruption of fire, or luminous matter." For the evening of April 20, 1787, Herschel reported: "The volcano burns with greater violence than last night. I believe its diameter cannot be less than 3″ [three seconds of arc], by comparing it with that of the Georgian planet [Uranus]; as Jupiter was near at hand, I turned the telescope to his third satellite, and estimated the diameter of the burning part of the volcano to be equal to at least twice that of the satellite. Hence we may compute that the shining or burning matter must be above three miles in diameter. It is of irregular round figure, and very sharply defined on the edges. . . .

"The appearance of what I have called the actual fire or eruption of a volcano, exactly resembled a small piece of burning charcoal, when it is covered by a very thin coat of white ashes, which frequently adhere to it when it has been some time ignited; and it had a degree of brightness, about as strong as that with which such a coal would be seen to glow in faint daylight."[1]

Herschel's second report, the one to the Royal Society, had

[1] From Herschel's *Collected Works*, 1912 edition, which also contains the letter to De Magellan.

been called a "curiosity of lunar literature," and the fact that
Herschel did not make a formal report of the observation of
1783 (though he promised to do so) had been interpreted as
due to his realizing that he had made a mistake.

For the observation of 1783 he had used the designation
Mons Porphyrites of Hevelius; for the observation of 1787
he had given the distance from the northern rim of the
moon. In both cases it was the crater Aristarchus! And if one
observer uses the comparison with a "large polished gem
ruby," while the other speaks of a "small piece of burning
charcoal covered by a thin coat of white ashes," one cannot
help but conclude that they are describing the same thing.

Of course the Russians began to watch Aristarchus too
but apparently failed to see red spots, though Kozyrev on
one occasion saw what looked like evidence of a temporary
gas cloud. But the red spot was seen again by Japanese
astronomers in December, 1963.

An eclipse of the moon was due on December 30, 1963,
and the observers of the Rakurakuen Planetarium at Hiroshi-
ma began practicing the night before. At 15:55 Universal
Time (10:55 a.m., E.S.T.), as reported by Takeshi Sato, the
director: "Y. Yamada saw a large, distinct pink patch covering the southern part and outside of Aristarchus. This patch,
confirmed by all eight other observers, gradually spread toward Herodotus until clouds covered the moon at 16:26."

This is the first time that the spot was seen outside the
crater.

And the explanation of the phenomenon? There is none.
True, there has been some speculation that clouds of subatomic particles (protons) from the sun might cause some
minerals to glow with visible light, but at the moment this
can be considered only a scientific guess. If Herschel's observation is belatedly accepted as correct (and when Herschel
said he saw something, he saw it), the phenomenon occurred
while Aristarchus was not illuminated by the sun. On the
other hand, the Japanese observation, which took place one
day before full moon, when the sun was nearly vertically
above the lunar surface, sounds more like a spreading gas
cloud, luminous for yet unknown reasons.

Since the first American expedition to the moon will have
to land near the lunar equator, as will be explained later,
Aristarchus will be out of range for that expedition. But it
certainly is one area of the moon that will be investigated as
soon as it can possibly be done.

5. The Origin of the Moon

The question of why we have a moon would probably strike most people as being one of those superfluous questions like "Why are the oceans salty?" The logical answer seems to be "Well, they are," and this statement of fact looks like the end of the story. Actually both questions have meaning. The degree of saltiness of the oceans is one of the clues as to their age. If we had a complete and reliable answer to the question of why we have a moon, we could be far more certain about our ideas dealing with the origin of the solar system.

Just asking the question about the existence of the moon implies a certain degree of sophistication, which fact will become apparent if we imagine that this question has been asked at various times in history.

A Jewish writer of Old Testament days set down his own answer by saying that "The moon was created for the counting of the days," having the measurement of time and religious festivals in mind. Note that he did not write "for illuminating the nights," because he was well aware of the fact that the moon performs this function for only about one week per month.

The same question, asked during the night when Christopher Columbus saw the light on the water that convinced him that he would make landfall the following morning, would have been given a different answer. The questioner would have been told that there are seven "planets" in the sky, moving around the earth, the immovable center of the universe. These seven "planets" were the moon, Mercury, Venus, the sun, Mars, Jupiter, and Saturn; the moon just happened to be the nearest.

About a century later things had changed. Nicholas Copernicus had proved to those who were interested (not a large number of people) and who had the knowledge and

73

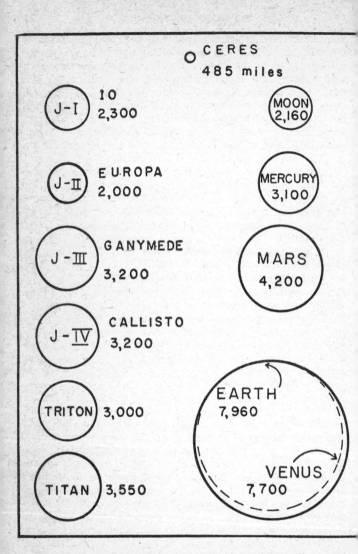

Fig. 20. The Largest Moons and the Smallest Planets. Three of the moons in our solar system are larger than the smallest planet (Mercury). The moons J-1 (for Jupiter-1) to J-IV can be seen with good field glasses if the sky is clear. Titan is the largest moon of Saturn and Triton the larger of the two known moons of Neptune. Ceres is the largest of the asteroids orbiting the sun between the orbits and Mars and Jupiter.

patience to read a difficult book (an even smaller number) that the sun occupied the center of the universe and that the earth was one of the planets, the third planet from the sun, with Mercury and Venus moving inside the earth's orbit. The next planet outside the earth's orbit was Mars. As for our moon, it could be said to move in the same orbit as the earth because it moved around the earth. In this respect earth was unique; no other planet had a moon (remember that Copernicus still belonged to the first era of astronomy, before the invention of the telescope).

Johannes Kepler, born almost precisely one century after the birth of Copernicus, felt perturbed about this fact. He wanted to find a reason. Since the earlier part of Kepler's lifetime also fell into the first era of astronomy, there was no way yet to determine the sizes of the planets. It could be that the earth was the largest of the planets and for this reason somehow "deserved" to have a moon. But Kepler was not satisfied with this reasoning and frankly rejoiced when Galileo Galilei announced in 1610 that he had discovered four large moons accompanying Jupiter. Earth was no longer mysteriously singled out; other planets had moons too. Kepler hoped for a simple numerical relationship; since the earth had one moon and Jupiter was now known to have four, the planet between earth and Jupiter, namely Mars, should have two. And the planet beyond Jupiter, Saturn, would have either six or eight moons.

Well, the solar system is not as orderly as Kepler thought. It so happens that Mars does have two moons, but Jupiter has a dozen and Saturn has nine. For about one and a half centuries after Kepler astronomers forgot philosophical reasoning for the joy of making actual discoveries. Five of the moons of Saturn were discovered in quick succession; one German and one Austrian thought they had seen at least one of the two moons of Mars predicted by Kepler, and Giovanni Domenico Cassini thought he had found a moon of Venus, a mistake that was not completely cleared up until the early part of the current century. But all these discoveries added up to a specific problem: if somebody should undertake the task of trying to explain the origin of the solar system, he not only had to account for the planets but also had to explain about a dozen large moons.

The attempt was made twice in the course of the eighteenth century, in 1755 by the German philosopher Immanuel Kant and in 1796 by the French mathematician Pierre Simon, Marquis de Laplace. Both assumed that a "nebula" consisting of gas and cosmic dust would, in the course of time, condense to form a solar system. This is still the prevailing thought, but a fair amount of detail over which both Kant and Laplace stumbled—partly because many facts were then still unknown, partly because the mathematical tools were inadequate for the problem—has been rearranged in the meantime. The main difference between the old and new theories about the origin of the solar system is this: in the old theories the nebula was supposed to condense into a luminous fast-rotating body that finally became our sun. Because of the fast rotation, matter was thrown out into space from the equator of the early sun, forming rings which were then supposed to condense into the planets. These theories made the sun older than the planets and assumed the latter to be literally children of the sun. In the current theories it is assumed that there were several centers of condensation in the original nebula; one of them was naturally the biggest. That one became the sun, while the small ones in time turned into planets. In these theories the sun and the planets are of about the same age, and the difference in construction and behavior is due only to their different masses. In these modern theories the moons were still smaller condensations, so that the total number of planets and moons in a solar system depends on the number of condensation centers that originally formed in the nebula.

So far it looks as if the story of the origin of our moon progressed neatly from early and somewhat fumbling guesses to the recent and mathematically refined theories.

But just the story of our own moon—nobody paid any attention to the other moons in the solar system—had several strange interludes during the nineteenth century. The first one originated with the Danish mathematician and astronomer Peter Andreas Hansen.

Hansen began, in about 1838, to calculate very careful tables of the orbit of the moon; these tables were published in London in 1857. As has been explained in one of the preceding chapters, the orbit of the moon looks like a closed ellipse only on diagrams. In reality the orbit of the moon, like that of the earth, is an ellipse around the sun. The influence of the sun's gravity on the moon is about twice as large as the influence of the earth's gravity, but the influence of the earth is enough to cause the two orbits to be intertwined. Even this very condensed description of the true conditions shows that a calculation of the moon's orbit cannot possibly be a simple matter. Hansen had a difficult task ahead of him when he began work on his lunar tables, and his only tools were his brain and tables of logarithms, some of which he had to calculate himself before he could go on. Electronic computers were more than a century in the future, and although a few early mechanical computers existed, they were cumbersome to operate and their reliability was doubted.

Small wonder that Hansen came across minor discrepancies all the time. After a while he began to wonder whether these discrepancies might not all be due to a common cause, in other words to an unknown factor. Thinking about the problem of which factor might be unknown, he had a sudden insight. He treated the moon as if it were a sphere, with Newton's rule that a spherical body in space behaved as if all its mass were concentrated in the center of the sphere. But what if the moon were not spherical? In that case its geometrical center and its center of gravity would be two different things, and that might well account for the steady "errors" he encountered. But the moon's disk was round; there could be no doubt about that. Therefore, if the moon were not a sphere, it could only be elongated along the line of sight from earth. That resulted in an egg-shaped moon, always pointing its narrower end in the direction of the earth.

But if that was the case, the unknown far side of the

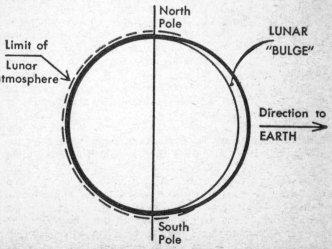

Fig. 21. Hansen's Moon. The shape of the moon as imagined by Peter Andreas Hansen and assuming a tall, earth-pointing bulge.

moon might differ considerably from the near side, which we can see. The far side might have an atmosphere and possibly open water, for all we could see was the surface of a gigantic high plateau that was higher than the lunar atmosphere.[1]

Since Hansen was an important man in his time, his opinions were listened to, but this particular idea met with little acceptance. The large moons of the other planets were spherical and it was difficult to believe that our own moon should be built in such a peculiar manner. It was the American astronomer Professor Simon Newcomb who, near the end of the nineteenth century, definitely disproved Hansen's guess.

The other strange interlude in the history of our moon came late in the nineteenth century; to be specific, in 1898. In that year Sir George Howard Darwin, one of the sons of the famous biologist Charles Darwin, published a book with the rather neutral title: *The Tides and Kindred Phenomena in the Solar System*. The book contained the assertion that the moon was literally a child of the earth, that both at some time during the dim past had formed one body. The earth, according to Sir George H. Darwin, had rotated at the rate of once every four hours at the time and its just-formed body was still completely molten. The fast rotation caused a bulge to form so that the earth for some time was pear-shaped. Then the bulge separated and was thrown off into space to become the moon. The tidal forces produced on both bodies by the mutual tugging went to work. The rotation of the earth was reduced to once in twenty-four hours; the smaller moon, while receding from the earth all the time, was braked to one rotation per revolution.

Several critics pointed out immediately that it could not possibly work that way. If you had a rapidly spinning (and still molten) earth, the planet might be flattened by the fast

---

[1] Hansen's idea did not become well known outside astronomical circles; it was mentioned casually in some popular books during the latter part of the nineteenth century. It did inspire a major science-fiction novel by the Polish author Jerczy von Zulawski (published circa 1906 and unfortunately never translated) and it did serve once more for the first major space-travel movie, Fritz Lang's *The Girl in the Moon* (released in October, 1929), which takes place on the far side of the moon. Air, but not open water, was assumed because, as Lang said at the time, "I cannot play long scenes in diving suits." The diving suits of the time effectively concealed the actors' faces, and since the film was without sound, the different characters could not be identified by their voices (See Plate 22.)

rotation and if it spun fast enough might even assume a shape like a thick lens. But it would not produce a single bulge in one place on the equator.

While most European experts rejected Darwin's hypothesis without much delay, Darwin found a staunch supporter in the person of the American astronomer William H. Pickering. The main reason why Pickering thought that the moon and the earth had once been united was that the Pacific Ocean is fairly circular in outline. Pickering said that the Pacific was the "scar" caused by the birth of the moon. He pointed out that the moon's density corresponds to the density of the earth's outer crust (but not to the average density of the whole earth) and that a segment of the earth, of the size of the Pacific Ocean and with a thickness of about thirty miles, would be about equal to the mass of the moon. Of course the "scar" is not thirty miles deep anymore; it was more or less filled in by magma from greater depths and partly by a movement of the continents remaining on earth after this enormous piece broke away. For the subsequent history, gradual recession of the moon and mutual braking, Pickering agreed with Darwin.

Of course nobody believes any of this anymore. There is no way in which a large piece can break away from a planet without causing more than comparatively minor damage to the rest of it. The idea that the moon might be a child of the earth is as obsolete as an idea can be.

Fig. 22. Typical Terrestrial Volcano. (Mt. Mayon, Luzon, Philippines.)

There are only two possibilities for the moon's origin. One is that it was formed near the earth from a much smaller center of condensation in the original nebula. The other possibility is that it was formed from a smaller condensation center a long distance from the earth and was later "captured" by the earth and forced into its current orbit.

Such a capture of a smaller body by a larger one is possible, though highly unlikely. It would be a most unusual event, but the idea cannot be completely rejected; it is just possible that it happened that way.

Does the moon offer any clues as to which is more likely? The orbital motion of the moon does not permit a decision; since it is just the result of masses and distances, it reveals nothing about the past.

Well, since the orbit of the moon does not contain any useful hints, how about its surface features? The main features, remember, are the *maria*, the ringwalls of the craters, the rays and rills, and the domes, with the craters being the most numerous feature.

How did the craters of the moon originate? The first man to have thought about this problem seems to have been the English mathematician, physicist, and astronomer Robert Hooke, of whom it has been said that he would be far more famous than he is if he had not had the misfortune to be a contemporary of Sir Isaac Newton and Dr. Edmond Halley. Hooke reasoned that the area now marked by a crater was once molten and that volcanic gases formed large bubbles in the molten rock, much larger than any bubbles of that kind could be on earth because of the lesser gravity. Finally the bubbles either burst or, after hardening, collapsed, producing the ringwall shape we now see.

If the lunar "craters" had diameters of a hundred feet or smaller, the bubble hypothesis might still be seriously discussed, but since the diameters of the most typical craters run from thirty to sixty miles, it simply does not work. Even under the lesser lunar gravity a thirty-mile bubble of molten rock is an impossibility.

All through the eighteenth century the craters of the moon were believed to be what their name implied, namely volcanoes, most of them dead. Sir William Herschel, when he saw a luminous spot on the moon, did not hesitate for a moment to speak of a "blazing volcano," and there was occasional speculation that the stones that some people claimed to have seen falling from the sky might be due to eruptions of lunar volcanoes.

A new thought about the lunar craters was published in 1828 by a German astronomer of Dutch ancestry, Franz von Paula Gruithuisen. He said that many lunar craters looked to him as if they had been caused by the impact of large meteorites. Another German, K. L. Althans, who was a mining expert with military experience, joined in by saying that the lunar craters reminded him of the marks left on armor plate by solid shot if the shot had not been powerful enough to break through the armor plate. Althans even experimented; he prepared large pans of fairly thin plaster of paris with water and dropped musketballs and the small cannonballs then known as grapeshot into them. Quite often he obtained shapes that closely resembled lunar craters.

But the opinions expressed by Gruithuisen and Althans did not cause a debate yet; the main interest in astronomical circles was directed at charting the lunar craters; a discussion about their origin could wait.

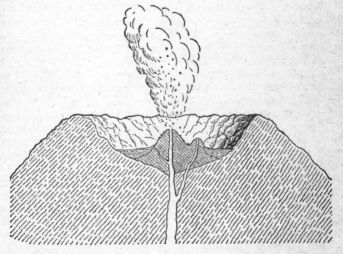

Fig. 23. Cross section through a lunar crater, as imagined by James Nasmyth.

The two men who opened the discussion were the two authors of the book *The Moon, Considered as a Planet, a World and a Satellite*, James Nasmyth, an engineer, and James Carpenter, "late of the Royal Observatory, Greenwich," as it says on the title page. In the preface of the book they announced what they intended to do. "Much valuable labour has been bestowed upon the topography of the moon, and this subject we do not pretend to advance. Enough has also been written for the benefit of those who desire an acquaintance with the intricate movements of the moon in space; and accordingly we pass this subject without notice. But very little has been written respecting the moon's physiography, or the causative phenomena of the features ... that the surface of our satellite presents for study."

Both men started out with the firm conviction that something called a crater should be a crater; hence the ringwalls had to be explained as being due to lunar volcanism. But there were some difficulties. A typical volcano has a shape that shouts "volcano" a long distance off. It is a tall cone with gently sloping sides (Fig. 22) built up by the action of the volcano itself over a long time. The crater on top of the mountain is a circular hole with a diameter that is small (around ten percent) compared to the diameter of the volcano's base. Nasmyth and Carpenter had to admit that no volcano looking like Mt. Etna or Mt. Fuji existed anywhere on the moon.

It is true that we have a type of formation on earth that both results from volcanic action and resembles a lunar crater. Geologists have a special name for it; they call it a "basal wreck," and it always indicates a former catastrophe. The explanation of a basal wreck is this: the volcano in question had been active in the past but had then become dormant. The lava filling the shaft from the interior to the mouth of the crater had slowly hardened into a solid plug. But then the volcano became active again and pressure began building up in the interior below the base. If one of the sides of the ancient volcano had a weak spot, the gases and lava might force their way out through this weak spot, creating a secondary crater. But if the mountain did not have a pronounced weak spot the pressure would continue building up until it was powerful enough to lift the whole central area of the mountain, spewing it up into the air in the process of a colossal explosion. The result would be a shallow circular depression surrounded by the lower portions of the old mountain—the basal wreck.

While a basal wreck did resemble a lunar ringwall, Nasmyth and Carpenter rejected this explanation, and with good reason. It was impossible to believe that all the lunar volcanoes had gone through the successive stages resulting in a basal wreck. If one had, say, one ringwall for every three intact volcanic cones (all of which might now be dormant or dead), the idea might be discussed. But one could not have basal wrecks exclusively.

Therefore, they reasoned, volcanic activity on the moon must have been different from the volcanic activity we still have on earth, possibly due to the lesser gravity. The lunar volcanoes, they argued, did not eject heavy, slow-moving, and sluggish flows of lava, but discharged volcanic ash at a high velocity, producing a fountainlike effect that deposited the ash in a circle some distance from the discharge hole. After the outer ringwall had thus been built up, the activity lessened and a cinder cone rose in the center. Sometimes liquid magma welled up and covered the crater floor, including the cinder cone, in which case a flat-floored crater was formed. In one case, Wargentin, the welling up of the magma continued until the ringwall that had first been formed was brimful.

Of course in a few cases the volcanic activity was not powerful enough to produce a distant ringwall; then a fairly normal cinder cone would be built up, for example the isolated mountain Pico in the *Mare imbrium*. A very similar though much smaller volcanic mountain could be found on earth, located at the end of a street in Tenerife. (Plate 4).

Mr. Nasmyth drew a number of very pretty diagrams, showing how his lunar volcanoes began gently, then produced the fountain spray, and then gradually petered out. The unfortunate fact was that such volcanic fountains simply have never been observed. Terrestrial volcanoes might eject large amounts of ash, but that ash then covers an area and the thickness of the ash layer is likely to be greatest near the crater hole unless a strong wind was blowing at the time of the eruption. On the moon, because of the lesser gravity, the ash would be distributed over a larger area, but it would still be just an ash layer, not a pretty ringwall of nearly precise circularity. Nor would there be any reason why a ringwall that has been formed by the fountain effect should comply with "Schröter's rule." The central peak would almost invariably be higher than the ringwall.

Between them Nasmyth and Carpenter had produced an interesting and beautiful book, but as an explanation of the origin of the features of the moon it was a plain failure.

A number of researchers, of whom the German H. Ebert in 1895 probably was the first, wondered whether the tide-raising forces of the nearby earth might not be held responsible for the ringwalls. The reasoning was based on two assumptions, both of which seemed correct at the time. The first assumption was that the moon, at the time of crater formation, still rotated on its axis faster than it does now, say at the rate of once in a hundred hours. The second assumption was that the body of the moon was still molten magma, with only a comparatively thin outer crust. The crust certainly could be assumed to have holes and weak spots. Now, when the earth was overhead, the magma would come out of such a hole and flood a roughly circular area of varying size. At the extreme edge of the flooded area some of the magma would harden; at the same time, a thin slice of the solid crust would be melted by the heat of the magma resting on it temporarily. The magma, once the earth was beyond the horizon, would flow back into the center hole, leaving a ring of hardened material and a faint depression inside the ring. Next time the earth was overhead the process would be repeated; the ringwall would grow a bit higher and thicker and the depression inside the ringwall would be a little deeper.

It was a concept that could be tested by experiment. Ebert himself used an open glass bowl filled with Wood's Metal that has a melting point of only one hundred and fifty-five degrees Fahrenheit. The bowl was kept hot at the bottom, but the surface of the metal was permitted to solidify. By means of a simple hand-operated pump some liquid metal was forced through a small hole in the "frozen" surface to the top of it, and after a short time—before it had congealed —was drawn back into the bottom of the bowl. If this was repeated a dozen times or so, something quite similar to the lunar crater was the result. By the time I was old enough to take an interest in such things, Ebert's original models had been melted down, but in the meantime others had repeated the experiment. I have seen several very nice craters made of molten sulfur by this method, one or two where thin plaster of paris had been used, and even one made of chocolate!

A present-day selenologist would challenge the idea on two grounds. One is that we don't know whether the moon ever was a completely molten body. The other is that we cannot be certain that tidal forces would work that way, since the earth's gravitational pull acts on the moon as a whole and not on its (assumed) liquid interior only.

But in addition to Robert Hooke's gigantic bubbles, Nasmyth's and Carpenter's volcanic fountains, and Ebert's and company's tidal basins there was one more thought—the impact theory, first proposed by Franz von Paula Gruithui-sen. After Gruithuisen and Althans, the English astronomer Richard Anthony Proctor had thought about it and had come to the conclusion that at least "most of the smaller craters of the moon" were due to meteoritic impact. That had been in 1873. Only four years later a German architect, A. Meydenbauer, spoke in favor of the impact theory and another two years later a German father-and-son team followed suit.

It was an unusual father-and-son team, considering the fact that they concerned themselves with the surface features of the moon. The father, Heinrich W. J. Thiersch (pronounced *Teersh*), was a professor at a German university, holding the chair of theology. His son, August Thiersch, was a practicing architect. They declared that they were convinced that the lunar craters, and even the *mare* plains, were the result of the impact of meteorites of all sizes. But the idea that something called a crater had to be volcanic was too deeply entrenched at the time so that their careful reasoning was mentioned in astronomical works as an interesting but curious (with all the opprobrium that this term can assume) thought.

The American geologist G. K. Gilbert, who published his ideas in the bulletin of the Philosophical Society of Washington in 1892, advanced very similar arguments and received much the same treatment.

Since the publication of the ideas of the Thiersch team and G. K. Gilbert's paper "The Moon's Face," two areas of the world have been won over to the impact theory by two books. In the United States Ralph E. Baldwin's *The Face of the Moon,* published in 1949, marked the turning point. In continental Europe it was a work by Alfred Wegener, a geologist, entitled *The Origin of the Lunar Craters,* published in 1949.[2]

Alfred Wegener started out with a fundamental observation. Experiments performed by others and consisting of throwing tennis balls against panels of fresh mortar had occasionally produced small models of lunar craters, but only occasionally. If one assumed that the lunar craters actually were impact craters—an assumption much strengthened by the discovery of impact craters on earth since 1900—then

[2] The Lunar Section of the British Astronomical Association still holds out for volcanic origin, presumably on the grounds that an opinion held for centuries cannot be wrong, though it may require a few modifications.

something had to be wrong with the experiments. A little thought showed what had been done wrong: the earlier experimenters, beginning with Althans, had failed to pay enough attention to the type of physical forces acting during the experiment. Wegener made the distinction between "molecular forces" (especially the tensile strength of the material) and "mass forces" (mainly gravitation). Both are present whether a musketball splashes into fresh mortar or a mountain-sized meteorite crashes into the surface of the moon, but their ratios are different.

In a laboratory experiment the tensile strength of a lead or iron ball plays a large role and so does the surface tension of a mixture of plaster of paris and water. The mass force of gravitation does not count at all or appears only as a disturbing factor. But when it comes to the impact of a body weighing thousands of tons with an impact velocity of thirty miles per second, only mass forces count and the tensile strength of the impacting body becomes negligible. Therefore, Wegener reasoned, if a laboratory experiment is to yield a good replica of an impact crater, it should be performed with material that has no tensile strength. For the practical reason that it could be hardened later if desired, Wegener picked cement dust, both for the "meteorite" and for the "lunar surface." On a laboratory scale fine powder should behave in the same manner as do rocks in a large-scale event.

The experiment itself was quite simple: a metal tray was covered with an inch-thick layer of dry cement powder, carefully smoothed out. Then a soupspoonful of cement dust was dropped on this surface from the height of about a yard. Even the very first drop resulted in a crater looking very much like Copernicus (except for the central peak, which was missing in the laboratory model), and subsequent experiments produced nearly all the variations that can actually be observed on the moon.[3] An elliptical crater was obtained by accident at first, but somebody had noticed that the falling cement dust had split during the fall; it was then easy to make elliptical craters by having two "meteorites" hit simultaneously and closely together. The only known strongly elliptical impact crater on earth, near Henbury, in Australia, must have resulted from a meteorite that split apart during its passage through the earth's atmosphere.

[3] Model craters made by the author following Wegener's method are shown on Plate 12. The photographs were made by placing the tray in the shade of a building and illuminating it with slanting sunlight, reflected into the shade by an ordinary household mirror.

For a long time Wegener did not obtain a crater with a central peak, but even these could be produced by having the cement-dust layer representing the surface quite thin. The question "Just what happens to the meteorite?" had been in Wegener's mind all along, and in order to answer that question plaster of paris powder was substituted for cement dust, but for the "meteorite" only. The surprising result was that the whole "crater" showed white, with white splashed outside the ringwall. The crater was carefully hardened by means of a fine water spray and then a cross section was made. Examination of the cross section not only showed what had happened to the meteorite but also disclosed the process of crater formation.

The plaster of paris formed a thin layer covering the crater floor and was more thickly distributed along the inner edge of the ringwall, and a fair amount of it had been carried by its momentum across the ringwall as far as eight to ten crater diameters. What evidently happens during such an impact is that the meteorite shatters and that the kinetic energy is used up in scooping up ground material and moving it outward

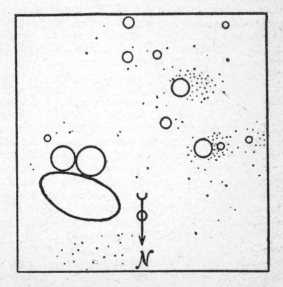

Fig. 24. Group of Impact Craters near Henbury, Central Australia. The largest crater of the group measures about 650 by 360 feet. Black dots indicate the places where meteoric iron has been found.

from the center of impact. Small wonder that "Schröter'
rule" applies so well, for the ringwall consists of material tha
has been scooped up and moved. Some material, meteorie
fragments as well as surface matter, will be carried across the
ringwall and will produce secondary craters such as have
been found on the moon around many of the major impact
craters. (Fig. 25)

The central peak seems to be surface material that stayed
put. In the experiments a central peak was formed when the
cement dust layer was thin; this might mean that those lunar
craters that show a central peak were formed in areas where
a solid layer of very hard rock is present at a low depth
below the surface. Terrestrial-impact craters do not help with
this question because they are all without a central peak.
They are also deeper (in comparison to their diameters) than
lunar craters. Both may be due to the fact that on earth there
is always moisture present, which is converted into water
vapor by the heat of the impact, so that a steam explosion
occurs simultaneously.

A careful look at the actual lunar craters shows clearly
that they must have been formed at different times. Some
look new, with sharp outlines such as those of freshly minted
coins. Others—the walled plain Clavius is a fine example—
show that they are old, with the scars of later impacts in their
interior as well as on the ringwall itself and with areas of the
original ringwall clearly worn, as if by erosion. But erosion
on the moon is not what it is on earth, since water is not
involved. Lunar erosion is the result of millions of years of
impacts of smaller meteorites down to the size of grains of
sand, plus the action of subatomic particles. That the craters

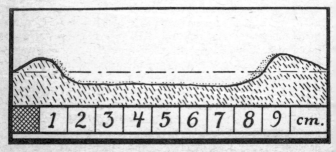

Fig. 25. Cross section of One of Wegener's Craters. This crater,
nine centimeters in diameter, was produced by using plaster of
paris. The distribution of the plaster is shown by the dots on the
crater floor and on the inside of the ringwall.

differ in age is only to be expected: the moon was not subjected to an enormous devastating salvo of large meteorites at one point in its career; it must have been a gradual process.

We can now go over the features of the lunar surface again, this time with short statements about their probable origins.

The ringwalled craters of all sizes are now accepted by most astronomers as impact craters, with large numbers of tiny craters near large ones considered to be secondary craters produced by the impact of debris thrown out when a large crater was formed.

The rays were considered all along by many astronomers as streaks of material thrown out during the formation of a large crater. More about the material of the rays is in the next chapter.

The rills, or clefts, are still unexplained. One theory has it that the interior of the moon expanded because of heating by radioactive substances so that the stiff outer shell cracked. But it is quite possible that the features which look alike when seen from the distance of the earth are not alike when it comes to close-up inspection. There may well be several kinds of rills formed by dissimilar processes.

The domes (and possibly a number of the very small craterlets) may be true volcanoes. Again, this cannot be decided by a view from earth, but a decision may not have to wait until an astronaut with a geologist's hammer walks around on the lunar surface. Soft-landed television devices or even photographs from satellites in low orbits around the moon may furnish the answer.

How about the dark plains, the *maria?* Because they are naked-eye objects and the craters are not, the impression that there must be a fundamental difference between them has taken root. Actually the two features overlap and blend. Yes, the *maria* are dark, but the sixty-mile crater Plato also has a dark floor. The walled plain Grimaldi, with a diameter of about one hundred and twenty-five miles, might have been called a *mare* if it were not difficult to observe because of its position near the moon's limb. But while Grimaldi has a dark floor, Clavius and Schickard, which are larger than Grimaldi, do not have a dark floor. On the other hand, the *Mare crisium* is circular, is dark-floored, and has twice the diameter of Clavius. The dark-floored Rainbow Bay, the *Sinus iridum* of the *Mare imbrium,* would certainly be considered to be a large crater, with a diameter of about one hundred and fifty miles, if only it were a complete crater.

Since the *maria* are of roughly circular shape and the smallest of them (*Mare crisium* and *Mare nectaris*) are not much larger than the largest of the walled plains, the *maria* must also be due to the impact of bodies, bodies of the size of the larger asteroids. It is thought, for example, that the *Sinus iridum* was a complete and large walled plain before the body that created the *Mare imbrium* united with the moon.

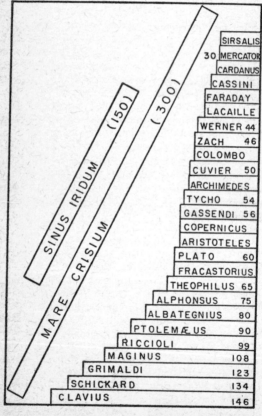

Fig. 26. *Sinus iridum, Mare crisium,* and Twenty-six Craters. The diameters of these formations, given in miles, show that the normal craters, the walled plains, and the *maria* seem to differ in size only.

The visible portion of the moon shows the traces of the impact of about a dozen bodies of the size of large asteroids, about one hundred and fifty bodies that can be called small asteroids and many thousands of large meteorites. These large numbers suggest that the moon was not just the unfortunate target of a cosmic barrage. They suggest that this was the way the body of the moon was formed, by the slow accretion of smaller bodies of all sizes. Some experts think that the body of the moon was never completely molten—as is generally assumed to have been the case with the earth at an early date—but that only local melting in and near the area of enormous impacts, the *mare* plains of today, took place.

Theorizing about details at the present moment may be called "too late" as well as "too early." Too early because the next two decades will provide us with a flood of information gathered on the moon itself. Too late because the time when theorizing was all one could do, when there was no real hope of ever reaching the moon, has been over for a few decades.

Just two things should be pointed out. Since the *Mare imbrium* is just the largest impact scar on the visible side of the moon, the mountains around the *mare,* the Alps, the Apennines, the Caucasus, and so forth, have to be looked at as portions of an enormous ringwall that is not different in origin from smaller ringwalls only a few score miles across. The other point to be made is that the supposed origin of the moon from the accretion of smaller bodies makes it likely that the moon was formed while traveling more or less in the same orbit it now has. The Thiersch father-and-son team more than three quarters of a century ago advanced the suggestion that the moon might originally have been a ring around the earth. In such a ring, formed of bodies of greatly varying sizes, the body that happens to be the largest will in time sweep up all the others. Alfred Wegener nearly half a century ago also thought that the earth started out with a ring. This particular problem will not be answered even by the most thorough explanation of the moon. We may be able to verify that the moon is the result of slow accretion. If this is verified as a fact, we will be able to find out whether the moon was ever completely molten or not.

But whether it once was a ring of earth will forever remain a subject of speculation.

6. Ranger to the Moon

At 12:45 p.m., Eastern Standard Time, the six-and-one-half-hour countdown of the big Atlas-Agena rocket on the launch pad of Complex 12 at Cape Kennedy went into its last five minutes. The date was July 28, 1964.

Eight seconds after 12:50 p.m. the countdown reached zero and the thunderclap of the ignition of three powerful rocket engines traveled across the cape area. The rocket, lifting off vertically, soon disappeared from sight. The two booster engines dropped off on schedule but the so-called sustainer engine—the one in the middle—kept burning. At the time the sustainer shut down the velocity was 12,600 miles per hour (3.5 miles per second). Then the Agena-B rocket took over, increasing the velocity to 17,500 miles per hour (4.86 miles per second) and the Agena-B rocket, with Ranger VII as payload in its nose, was in orbit 115 miles above sea level. It coasted in orbit for almost half an hour; then the rocket engine was reignited and burned until the speed had climbed to 24,525 miles per hour (6.806 miles per second), which put the spacecraft into the "moon corridor," the preselected flight path to the moon. Tracking results indicated that the spacecraft would reach the moon, even if nothing else were done.

On the ground hopes and worries were distributed in about equal amounts. Takeoff, coasting, and insertion into the "moon corridor" had been just about perfect, with the velocity of insertion differing by just four miles per hour from the theoretically perfect value. But takeoff, coasting, and insertion had been perfect too in January, 1964, with Ranger VI, and although Ranger VI had reached the moon at the predicted time and in the predicted area, it had been a failure. Its television cameras that had been supposed to take close-up pictures of the moon had failed to come to life.

Would Ranger VII be a repeat performance of Ranger VI? All the tests that could be made said that Ranger VII would perform. But could one be sure?

While the spacecraft was on its way a decision about the so-called midcourse correction was made on the ground. Several promising impact areas had been selected in advance; it was now a question of deciding which one of these impact areas should be used. The decision was in favor of an area, elliptical in shape and measuring roughly three hundred by fifty miles, near the crater Guericke. The Goldstone, California, radar sent instructions to the spacecraft from 3:54 to 3:58 a.m., Eastern Standard Time, on July 29. These instructions were not to be carried out at once but were merely impressed on the memory circuits in the spacecraft. At 4:40 a.m. the spacecraft's transmitter was ordered to switch from a directional antenna at its base to the omnidirectional antenna on top. That done, the directional antenna could be moved aside so that it would not be in the exhaust blast of the rocket engine that made the midcourse correction. At 5:00 the radio command went out to execute the instructions given earlier.

The first maneuvers did not yet alter the velocity; they were devoted to adjusting the "attitude" (position) of the spacecraft. Then the midcourse motor fired for fifty seconds

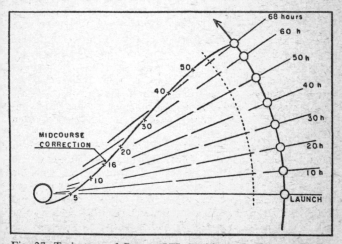

Fig. 27. Trajectory of Ranger VII. Positions of the moon in its orbit and positions of Ranger VII along its trajectory are shown at ten-hour intervals, counting from the moment of liftoff.

(from 5:27:09 to 5:29:59 a.m., E.S.T.), and by 5:58 all the maneuvers had been completed. Ranger VII was on course, moving with the proper velocity for impact near Guericke; the solar panels were wide open to the sun's rays for generating electric current; and there was firm radio contact between the spacecraft and the earth.

Impact was predicted for 8:25:49 a.m. on July 31.

At Cape Kennedy the clocks read 8:00 a.m., E.S.T., when the critical minutes approached. At Pasadena, California, where scientists and the press were assembled to check on the outcome of the flight, it was very early in the morning. Soon after 8:00 a.m. (Eastern Standard Time, as are all the figures to follow), things began to happen.

At 8:07:30 the signal from Ranger VII was fed into the loudspeakers of the auditorium; it appeared as a quavering, fairly high note. Only half a minute later the first announcement came:

8:08	"Channel F cameras [two wide-angle cameras] are in full power mode. All recorders at Goldstone recording station are in operation. The signal is strong and clear."
8:10	"Preliminary analysis confirms we are receiving pictures."
8:11	"Channel P cameras in warm-up mode" [four narrow-angle cameras].
8:12	"Channel P cameras in full power."
8:12:30	"Receiving signals from P cameras. Receiving signal from F cameras. Goldstone all go on all recorders."
8:15	"F and P still excellent. We are receiving pictures."
8:15:30	"All cameras are in operation. No interruption. It appears all six cameras are functioning."
8:18:30	"The video signal described as excellent. Impact due in seven minutes."
8:20	"We are receiving pictures from both systems."
8:22	"No interruption in signals. No interruption in reception. Entire system remains go, as it has since launch."
8:24	"Video strength continues high. All six cameras continue to operate. All recorders continue to operate. One minute to impact. We are receiving pictures all the way."
8:25	"All cameras are functioning. Twenty seconds to impact . . . ten seconds to impact. We are receiving pictures to the end."

8:25:49 "Impact!" [The quavering note stopped abruptly, its source having been destroyed.]

Ranger VII had completed the trip to the lunar surface in 68 hours, 35 minutes, and 45 seconds. The cameras had been in operation for the last 18 minutes of the flight, during which time 4,136 pictures had been taken and transmitted to earth, the F cameras taking pictures at 2.5-second intervals and the P cameras at intervals of only 0.2 seconds.

At Goldstone the signals were recorded on tape. The tape was later calibrated as to time, so there is no doubt at what instant a given picture was taken. The tape was then duplicated and also transferred to thirty-five-millimeter film. But during the transmission Polaroid pictures had been snapped off the TV screens. Even the quick Polaroid prints immediately showed that the quality of the pictures sent back by Ranger VII was far superior to the quality of the pictures obtained by the Russians in October, 1959. The pictures from Russia's Cosmic Rocket III had shown very little contrast because the sun had been high over the lunar areas photographed by the rocket. They had also been blurred by static that interfered with transmission and they had been few in number. In fact, the only reason that the Russian pictures showed lunar formations astronomers had never seen before was that areas not visible from earth were photographed.

The thousands of pictures that poured out of the cameras of Ranger VII were sharp and clear. They needed no processing other than enlarging. The first pictures taken, from a distance of slightly over sixteen hundred miles above the moon, could be directly compared with photographs obtained by astronomical observatories in the usual manner. As Ranger fell closer and closer to the moon's surface, detail began to show up that could never be seen by any earth-based telescope. Smaller and smaller craters appeared on the pictures, and the very last picture to be transmitted had been taken about one thousand feet above the surface. It showed tiny craters, just about one yard in diameter. And since the sun was only twenty-three degrees of arc above the horizon for the landscape photographed, the craters, ridges, and craterlets produced nice sharp shadows, again like pictures taken from earth by astronomical observatories.

But since the Russian attempt to photograph the moon from space took place about five years before the American success, a short description of the Russian method and its results is in order at this point.

When Russian scientists planned the shot which was then

labeled Cosmic Rocket III, they evidently had to weigh the things they wanted to do against the things they could do. They decided against a shot for impact because that would not give them enough time; besides, they had already demonstrated their ability to hit the moon at an earlier date.[1]

They were, like all other selenographers, burning with curiosity about the appearance of the far side of the moon, and the best method for obtaining such pictures would have been to make their instrument package orbit the moon. Now, this requires a special maneuver. A rocket which has covered the distance to the moon and has passed its orbit is too fast to become a satellite of the moon. It will have to be slowed down by means of retrofiring rockets when in the vicinity of the moon so that it becomes slow enough to be held by the moon's weak gravitational pull. The Russians could no doubt have incorporated a retrofiring rocket in their instrument package. That they dismissed this idea then was probably due to another factor: if their instruments were in orbit

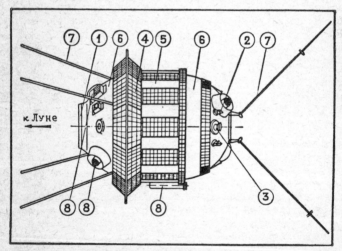

Fig. 28. Cosmic Rocket III. Russian outline drawing of the instrument package of their picture-taking shot around the moon. The numbers indicate the following: (1) window for the cameras, (2) attitude-control nozzles, (3) solar sensor, (4) solar panels, silicon converters, (5) temperature-control panels, (6) heat-insulating panels, (7) antennas, and (8) sensor for instruments inside. The Russian words above the arrow mean "to the moon."

[1] See Appendix.

around the moon, the pictures would have to be transmitted over a distance of 240,000 miles. That distance may have seemed too great for picture transmission with the equipment then available.

For all these reasons they decided on an interesting compromise. They would put their instruments into an orbit around the earth along an ellipse long enough to have its apogee at a greater distance than the moon's orbit. By timing such a shot correctly, the spacecraft would pass behind the moon—as seen from earth—while the sun was illuminating the far side. Then the spacecraft would approach the earth again and transmission would take place while it traversed the perigee sector of its orbit. Naturally, after going through its perigee, it would climb outward again toward apogee. The apogee distance would be the same as before, but this time the moon would not be nearby, having moved to a different part of its own orbit. Hence only the first passage could be utilized for picture-taking. However, every subsequent perigee approach could be used to have the first transmission repeated for as long as there was electrical power available. Cosmic Rocket III was, strictly speaking, not a lunar probe but an artificial earth satellite with a highly unusual orbit, more elongated than any other satellite orbit before or since. As a matter of fact, the satellite climbed to such a distance in the earth's gravitational field that one might say that it approached its edge; when it was near apogee the sun's gravitational

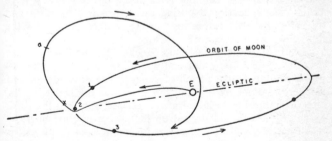

Fig. 29. The Orbit of Cosmic Rocket III. (1) shows the position of the moon at launch, (2) shows the moment of closest approach when the orbit of the rocket was both changed and tilted, (3) shows the position of the moon when the rocket reached apogee (marked by the letter α), and (4) shows the moon's position at the time the pictures were transmitted to earth. The pictures were taken after the rocket had passed the moon and reached the point marked by X. The final orbit was nearly vertical to the ecliptic.

field produced very pronounced perturbations, which made calculation difficult.

The experiment proceeded essentially as planned. Takeoff of the multistage rocket was on October 4, 1959—the second anniversary of Sputnik I—and the lower stages were left behind as scheduled. After the top stage had used up its fuel a total of 4,037 pounds was on its way to a rendezvous with the moon. Of this total, the casing of the top rocket stage accounted for 3,423 pounds. The overall weight of the scientific satellite was 614 pounds; the weight of the cameras and scientific instrumentation was 345 pounds. Instrumentation carried consisted of two cameras, the mechanism for developing the film, the transmitter, a trigger device for turning on the cameras by radio command, an automatic temperature control system, and, as the Russians put it, "other scientific devices."

Cosmic Rocket III reached the vicinity of the moon on October 6, 1959, and the cameras were turned on when it was forty thousand miles from the target. Closest approach to the moon took place at 9:16 p.m., E.S.T., on October 6 (48 hours and 16 minutes after launch), when the distance between the instrument capsule and the moon's *center* was only 4,372 miles. The orbit was violently disturbed by the moon (Fig. 29) but that had been foreseen. Picture-taking began when a part of the visible hemisphere would still show up in the picture (for reference and alignment with known features) and was continued for forty minutes. They were automatically developed during the return trip to earth and transmitted shortly before the satellite reached perigee for the first time, on October 18, 1959.

The final orbit of Cosmic Rocket III had an apogee distance of 292,000 miles and a perigee distance of 24,840 miles, with an orbital period of about fifteen days. Because of the perturbations by the sun, this orbit was not stable, so the satellite, returning to its thirteenth perigee, ran into the earth (May 19, 1960) and burned up in the upper atmosphere.

Although the flight was successful, there were malfunctions in the equipment. The hope of repeated transmissions of the pictures obtained was not fulfilled; four days after the first transmission (on October 22), both transmitters fell silent. And it is known that at least one of the two cameras jammed after only a small number of exposures, variously reported as nine or fourteen. And although at the time of the experiment the excitement of getting pictures of the moon's far side made everybody disregard their quality, there is no way of avoiding the statement that the quality was surprisingly poor.

The area covered by the photographs comprises about seventy percent of the area that cannot be seen from earth. Naturally the Russians named a number of the clearer features. Thus a dark spot was named after the Russian rocket pioneer Konstantin Eduardovitch Tsiolkovsky, a mountain chain was named the Soviet Range, one other crater was named after the physicist Joliot-Curie, another black patch received the name *Mare moscovianum* (Moscow Sea), and still another crater was named after the early Russian scientist Mikhail Vasilievitch Lomonósov, one of the discoverers of the atmosphere of the planet Venus.

An American team under Ewen A. Witaker took a set of unretouched prints, cleaned them up, and assembled them, stating that the "Russian pictures are better than their interpretation of them." A number of Russian interpretations were revised. The *Mare moscovianum* actually is a *mare* plain and the crater Tsiolkovsky is probably a black-floored, walled plain. But the Soviet Range is probably just a ray system, whereas the crater Joliot-Curie is really the *Mare novum,* which was identified and named by the German astronomer Julius Franz around the turn of the century.

The flight of Cosmic Rocket III was a remarkable feat of pioneering and proved that the far side of the moon does not differ fundamentally from the visible side. But all the real work still remains to be done.

At the time Cosmic Rocket III went through its complicated orbit, the American space effort was in the process of being organized. The first orbital shots had been handled by the U.S. Navy (Project Vanguard) and by the U.S. Army (the Explorer satellites), as well as by the U.S. Air Force, which developed the space probes called Pioneer. All three services used the Air Force installation at Cape Canaveral in Florida, which later came to be called Atlantic Missile Range and which is now Cape Kennedy. But though the three services worked together very well—the newspaper cliche about service rivalry is true only at budget time—it became clear that a separate agency was needed. Soon after World War I a government agency to serve aviation had been established; it was named National Advisory Committee for Aeronautics—NACA. It had performed excellent work, but after World War II, aviation was so much on its own that it wasn't much needed anymore. In 1958 it was decided to reorganize the old NACA so that its activities would be expanded beyond the atmosphere into space. The new agency was named National Aeronautics and Space Administration—NASA.

NASA naturally inherited personnel, facilities, and projects from the armed services, among them a number of planned shots to the moon.

The early moon shots of the Pioneer series had been unsuccessful without exception (see list in Appendix), and it was concluded that the main reason for the lack of success had been that the carrier rockets had been too weak for the task. These carrier rockets had been the otherwise quite successful Thor rockets of the Air Force and Jupiter rockets of the Army, but when it came to carrying a lunar probe, their lifting capabilities were strained. It seemed that the newly developed, more powerful Atlas rocket of the Air Force would be the answer. The Atlas could carry more, hence more leeway for upper stages and instrumentation and even more leeway for minor mistakes.

The reasoning was correct, but one unavoidable fact got in the way of success: the Atlas was a new rocket of which not enough specimens had yet been fired to consider it reliable. Two Atlas-carried moon probes came to grief in 1959, and two more in 1960. In all four cases the upper stages had been Able rockets.

To improve the situation several things had to be done. One had to wait for the Air Force to make the Atlas more reliable. It probably was wise to have a more powerful upper stage; in the meantime the Agena rocket had been developed. And there could be no harm in designing a new type of spacecraft: the payloads of the Pioneer shots had been designed along the lines of earth-orbiting artificial satellites. For deep-space work a special design was desirable, and the first Ranger was conceived, looking very much like the successful Ranger VII. But success was half a dozen tries in the future. Ranger I was fired on August 23, 1961. The flight plan was to put the spacecraft into a parking orbit first, then restart the Agena and put Ranger I into an elliptical orbit around the earth, with a perigee only a few hundred miles from the ground but an apogee at about twice the distance of the moon. Of course a passage near the moon was hoped for. The Atlas rocket, followed by a first burning of the Agena rocket, did put Ranger I into a parking orbit, with a perigee at 105.5 miles and an apogee at 312.5 miles. But then the

Agena refused to reignite, and Ranger I remained in its low orbit for six days. Then it reentered and burned up.

Ranger II was ready in November, 1961; it was supposed to do what Ranger I had been sent out to accomplish. Unfortunately it was a repeat of the first performance. The Agena engine shut down a few seconds only, producing a parking orbit with the apogee at 156 miles and a perigee at only 96 miles. If the Agena had restarted, the shot could still have been successful. But it did not and the spacecraft, put into orbit on November 18, 1961, remained in space for a little less than twenty-four hours.

Ranger III was fired on January 26, 1962. This time the goal was different. The Agena, after breaking out of the parking orbit, was to put the spacecraft into a trajectory leading to the moon, with a midcourse correction planned which would put it on a collision course. During the last quarter hour before impact, television pictures of the lunar surface were to be taken and transmitted. At a distance of seventy thousand feet from the moon an "impact capsule" with a retro-rocket was to be ejected. This retro-rocket was to be ignited at an altitude of fifty-two thousand feet above the moon and bring the impact capsule to a standstill approximately eleven hundred feet from the lunar surface. Falling under the moon's gravity, it would then strike the surface with an impact velocity of about one hundred and fifty miles per hour. The impact capsule was a thick balsa-wood capsule and the instruments inside had been designed to withstand an impact velocity more than twice as high as the one expected.

Takeoff was on January 26, 1962. This time the Agena rocket reignited properly, but it soon became clear that something else was wrong: the rocket was too fast. Ranger III traversed the distance to the moon's orbit in only fifty-one hours and as a consequence passed it a little more than twenty-three thousand miles ahead of the moon. Trying to get at least a few pictures, the operators on the ground switched on the TV cameras when the spacecraft was thirty-one thousand miles from the moon. But no pictures resulted; it is believed that the cameras functioned but that the transmitting antenna failed. Having passed in front of the moon and having enough velocity to escape from the earth's gravitational field, Ranger III went into orbit around the sun, an orbit slightly larger than the orbit of the earth. The perihelion of Ranger's orbit is 91,503,400 miles—about the same as the perihelion of the earth—but its aphelion is 108,133,850 miles from the sun, 13.6 million miles farther than the earth's aphelion.

Ranger IV, fired on April 23, 1962, produced the worst performance of all. It was to do what Ranger III had not done, and it was also equipped with an impact capsule. But after the Agena rocket had put Ranger IV in the proper trajectory, nothing happened. The solar panels remained folded; hence there was no electrical power except for one lone radio signal, fed by a battery. The high-gain antenna did not point toward earth as it was supposed to, and the commands beamed to the spacecraft were probably not even received. Ranger IV just plunged on toward the moon, probably tumbling, missed the leading edge of the moon by nine hundred miles, but did not reappear on the other side of the moon, so it must have made impact on the far side.

Ranger V was fired on October 18, 1962, and became another failure. Again all the early maneuvers—parking orbit, restart, and insertion into the lunar trajectory—went well. As far as anyone can tell the solar panels did unfold, but for an unknown reason they failed to deliver power, so the battery soon ran down. It missed the moon by only about 300 miles and then went into an orbit around the sun. Since there was no power at all, that orbit can only be calculated without any cross-check; it must be quite similar to the orbit assumed by Ranger III.

By that time, as can easily be imagined, a large number of people became quite nervous about the Ranger program and an investigation was ordered. Of course all planned future Ranger shots were postponed. The investigation showed that the concepts employed in the Ranger plans were quite sound but that simplification was called for in a number of systems. The directors of the Jet Propulsion Laboratory in California, which had built the Ranger spacecraft, did not like the investigation but did not have a very good record as far as this particular program was concerned. Therefore they agreed to leave out the impact capsule as an unnecessary complication, and they promised to accept recommendations. The result was Ranger VI, fired on January 30, 1964.

But, as has been mentioned early in this chapter, Ranger VI was a failure too. It performed just as planned all the way to the target, but then the all-important television cameras failed to work. (There is still no clear-cut explanation of this failure.) This time tempers came to a boil. The Jet Propulsion Laboratory is a division of the California Institute of Technology and is therefore not directly responsible to the government. One representative (Edward J. Gurney, of Florida) expressed the opinion that this was mere quibbling and that the laboratory was "for all practical purposes a prime contractor" which should be as closely supervised as any industrial contractor with a large-size government contract. Even the administrator of NASA, who had to preserve morale among the ranks of the laboratory's directors and scientists as much as possible under the circumstances, said that the next contract would require the laboratory to accept direction from NASA and would insist on tighter control and stricter testing.

Whether it was the tighter control or whether the streak of bad luck had simply run its course will never be decided, but Ranger VII did its job; it did take the pictures it was supposed to take.

Before we can talk about these pictures and their interpretation, Ranger VII should be described in a little more detail. The completed lunar probe looked like a gently tapering tall cone with two rectangular wings, but the backbone of the

FACT SHEET ON ATLAS-AGENA-B ROCKET

Height

Atlas rocket (first stage)	66 feet
Agena-B rocket	22 feet
Ranger with protective shroud	12 feet
Total height at takeoff, including adapters	approx. 104 feet

Weight

Atlas, fueled	approx. 260,000 pounds
Agena-B, fueled	approx. 16,000 pounds
Ranger, with shroud, etc.	approx. 1,000 pounds
Liftoff weight	approx. 277,000 pounds

Propulsion

Atlas-D rocket, thrust of booster engines (2) and sustainer engine (1), at sea level approx. 370,000 pounds

Agena-B rocket (1 engine), thrust in space 16,000 pounds

Fuels

Atlas-D rocket, RP-1 (kerosene-type fuel and liquid oxygen)

Agena-B rocket, inhibited red fuming nitric acid (IRFNA) and unsymmetrical dimethylhydrazine (UDMH)

FACT SHEET ON RANGER VII

Dimensions

During takeoff	Diameter	5	feet
	Height	8¼	feet
During transit	Span	15	feet
	Height	10¼	feet

Weights

Structure	91.15	pounds
Communications	38.71	pounds
Attitude control and autopilot	59.05	pounds
Data encoder	20.10	pounds
Central computer and sequencer	9.61	pounds
Propulsion	45.22	pounds
Power (solar panels, battery, etc.)	123.30	pounds
Miscellaneous equipment	37.85	pounds
Subtotal	424.99	pounds
TV cameras	37.95	pounds
Camera electronics	48.68	pounds
Video combiner	3.17	pounds
Sequencer	13.92	pounds
Batteries	86.24	pounds
Transmitters	70.24	pounds
Structure and miscellaneous	121.30	pounds
TV-system subtotal	381.50	pounds
Total weight	806.49	pounds

whole was a hexagonal framework of aluminum and magnesium tubing, called the "bus." The term is meant to indicate that it is an all-purpose structure that can accommodate many kinds of scientific and electronic devices, just as a real bus will accommodate all kinds of passengers. The various devices were attached to this framework, which was surmounted by the tapering television package that formed a truncated cone fifty-nine inches tall with a diameter of sixteen inches at the top and twenty-seven inches at the base. The omnidirectional antenna was placed on top of the television package.

The two solar panels were hinged to the base of the "bus"; each panel had an area of 12.2 square feet and held 4,896 solar cells that converted sunlight into electric current. Both panels together delivered two hundred watts of power. In addition to the solar panels there were two silver-zinc batteries to provide electric power while the panels were still folded. Each battery, providing 26.5 volts, was capable of providing the power for launch and for midcourse maneuvers. Another two batteries were built into the TV system; they would have been able to operate the cameras for one hour. (It is easy to see that the designers were not taking any chances with possible power failures.)

Also hinged to the bottom of the bus was a dish-shaped high-gain directional antenna; it has already been mentioned that this antenna had to be moved out of the way when the midcourse maneuver began.

The rocket device for the midcourse maneuver was located inside the frame of the bus. NASA Release No. 64-176 of July 23, 1964, described it as follows:

> The midcourse rocket motor is a liquid monopropellant engine weighing 46 pounds with fuel and nitrogen pressure gas system. Hydrazine fuel is held in a rubber bladder contained inside a doorknob-shaped container called the pressure dome. On the command to fire, nitrogen under 300 pounds of pressure per square inch is admitted inside the pressure dome and squeezes the rubber bladder containing the fuel.
>
> The hydrazine is thus forced into the combustion chamber, but because it is a monopropellant, it needs a starting fluid to initiate combustion and a catalyst to maintain combustion. The starting fluid, nitrogen tetroxide, is admitted into the combustion chamber by means of a pressurized cartridge. The introduction of the nitrogen tetroxide causes ignition, and the burning in the combustion chamber is maintained by the catalyst—aluminum oxide pellets stored in the chamber. Burning stops when the valves turn off nitrogen pressure and fuel flow.
>
> At the bottom of the nozzle of the midcourse motor are four jet vanes which protrude into the rocket exhaust for attitude control of the spacecraft during the midcourse

motor burn. The vanes are controlled by an autopilot linked to gyros.

The midcourse motor can burn in increments of as little as 50 milliseconds and can alter velocity in any direction in increments of 1.2 inches per second up to 190 feet per second. It has a thrust of 50 pounds for a maximum burn time of 98.5 seconds.

The midcourse motor served the purpose of increasing (or, after a turn-around, decreasing) the velocity of the spacecraft along the flight path. It could also have been used to change the direction of flight to some extent. But it was not used for merely changing the attitude of the spacecraft. That was the job of twelve cold-gas jets which were mounted in pairs on six different locations. Six of these jets, one of each pair, were connected to a titanium bottle holding 2½ pounds of nitrogen gas compressed to thirty-five hundred pounds per square inch. The other six jets were connected to another identical titanium bottle. There were therefore two separate attitude-control and stabilization systems, each of which could have handled the entire mission in case of failure of the other system. When one of these jets was called upon to act, it discharged the nitrogen gas under a pressure of fifteen pounds per square inch.

Since Ranger VII utilized sunlight as an energy source, the two solar panels had to be in such a position that they formed a right angle with the direction to the sun. In order to accomplish this, Ranger traveled "sideways" all the way, except for the midcourse maneuver and the terminal maneuver, when the cameras had to be turned toward the moon and nothing else counted anymore. In order to maintain the sunward position for the panel, four so-called "sun sensors" were mounted on four of the six uprights of the bus, plus two secondary sensors mounted on the backs of the solar panels. They were light-sensitive devices that informed the attitude-control system on whether they could "see" the sun. If they reported that they did, the attitude was correct; if they failed to "see" the sun, the position of the spacecraft had to be shifted until they did.

Finally, three radio transmitters were carried. Two of them were sixty-watt transmitters for the pictures; one handled the two wide-angle cameras, the other one the six narrow-angle cameras. The third transmitter was a three-watt receiver/transmitter which worked from the moment of insertion into the "corridor" to the moment of impact, transmitting engineering data about the functioning of all the components of the spacecraft.

They all functioned properly, and more than four thousand pictures resulted.

What have they taught us?

Let us begin with the trite statement that they have shown a multitude of tiny craters in the area of the *Mare nubium* photographed so that we can conclude that there must be millions of them over the expanses of the other *maria*. But the observed shapes of these craters are not always the same. A few are quite sharp and probably formed fairly recently, which in this case can still mean five thousand years ago. They are obviously due to impacts of meteorites from space. Other craters, with dimensions of from fifty to three hundred feet, look soft; they have, as one investigator phrased it, "a worn appearance." They are soft-looking because they have lost their sharp outlines after millions of years of bombardment with tiny sand-grain-sized meteorites from space. The fact that sharp "new" craters and "worn" craters can be seen on the same picture proves that they are actually worn and not just out of focus as one might otherwise suspect.

Many of the small craters seen in this area of the *Mare nubium* (astronomers are beginning to call this sector *Mare cognitum,* the "known sea," because of these detailed pictures) are clearly secondary craters which owe their existence not to direct meteorite impacts but to the impacts of matter that was splashed over the ringwall when a big crater was formed. Such material would strike with a much lesser velocity than an impact from space, resulting in a different shape. One large cluster of secondary craters in the area is believed to be the result of splashes from Copernicus.

Among the small craters one can be considered a prize. It is a very shallow crater with a large visible rock fragment in it. The fragment, presumably having originated during the Copernicus impact, is nearly three hundred feet in length, yet it did not bury itself deeply enough to disappear from view, proof that the lunar surface must be quite firm in that area.[2] Nobody doubts that there is a dust layer on the *Mare cognitum,* but the dust layer cannot be much more than an inch in thickness.

While approaching the moon, Ranger VII traversed a "ray"

---

[2] If that three-hundred-foot rock had been a meteorite originally it would have shattered on impact and produced a more typical crater. The very fact that it remained in one piece shows that it struck at a low velocity.

belonging to the ray system of Copernicus. The close-up pictures showed that older ideas about the rays had been wrong. Nasmyth and Carpenter had taken them to be cracks in the moon's crust, filled with glassy lava. Others had thought them to be streaks of powdery material. Another, older theory, bent on explaining the fact that only a few of the large craters had ray systems, had assumed that the rayless craters had been formed by stony meteorites and that the rayed craters betrayed that nickel-iron meteorites had impacted there. In this theory the rays were metal droplets condensed out of the metallic vapor produced by the impact. We now know that the rays are rubble in the literal sense. They are long streaks of rough debris produced by major impacts, with secondary craters marking the path of the ray. The ray systems are now considered to be the roughest surface areas of the moon, places that landing spacecraft have to avoid by all means.

The Ranger pictures are also interesting for what they *don't* show: they don't show smaller and smaller rills. Whatever caused the rills, it must have been something that does not work on a small scale.

Although the Ranger pictures have not solved all the problems, they have proved that the surface of the *mare* areas is hard enough to support a reasonable load. It will be safe to land on them, and then exploration of the moon can proceed from there.

Postscript: What Next?

The future exploration of the moon from the present until about 1970 has been carefully outlined by the various groups of researchers in charge of different projects and can therefore be foretold with reasonable precision.

The main question mark is the usual one: we don't know just what the Russians are planning to do and when they want to do it. There have been guarded Russian statements about sending a "tankette" to the moon, a small vehicle looking somewhat like a military tank (hence the name), which will travel around on the lunar surface, taking and transmitting television pictures of the landscape. After that, they have said, a manned expedition will be planned. This progression from (1) an impact shot, (2) a picture-taking shot, and (3) a soft-landed scouting device to (4) a manned landing is nothing but normal logic, so the Russian remarks can hardly be called a disclosure. No doubt they have plans that are far more detailed than that, but they have not published them.

Our own plans have been made public, but it must be admitted that the public that was supposed to be benefited by the publications is a bit confused. Part of this confusion—as I know because of questions I have to answer after lectures—is due to misunderstandings caused by lack of background information. Part of it is due to the fact that our space plans were disclosed piecemeal and the reader has trouble keeping different projects apart in his mind. And finally there is the fact that the United States has two sets of plans for space exploration.

The main set, comprising the whole moon program, earth-orbiting research satellites for scientific purposes, and space probes to the neighboring planets Mars and Venus—in short, everything scientific—is in the hands of NASA. But there is a smaller set of plans for space which is in the hands of the Air

Force. Its main announced goal is the creation of the MOL (Manned Orbital Laboratory), which is just what its name says: an earth-orbiting artificial satellite of sufficient size to be manned. The purpose of the MOL program is to determine what opportunities there are for men in space, mainly from the military point of view.

The carrier rocket under development for this program is Titan III, consisting of the liquid-fuel rocket Titan II with a takeoff thrust of 430,000 pounds, augmented by two 120-inch solid-fuel units with a thrust of more than one million pounds each. Titan III will be able to put a 20,000-pound payload into a low orbit just above the atmosphere. Of course there will have to be test shots before Titan III can be entrusted with its main job, that of lifting MOL vehicles into orbit. Twelve such shots are planned, and one of these twelve will have something to do with the moon. It will be fired for impact on the moon. The load that will strike the lunar surface will weigh 3,750 pounds—possibly large enough to produce a crater that can be photographed from earth.

But aside from this one shot, the exploration of the moon is the domain and the responsibility of NASA. One more Ranger spacecraft is available, and the first item on the agenda will be another picture-taking moon shot. Rangers VII and VIII were aimed at two different *mare* plains (one of which looks a little lighter in color than the other) to see whether all *maria* are alike. Apparently they are, and Ranger IX will therefore be aimed at a mountainous area, probably with an impact point in the interior of one of the large craters. The large light-floored craters are thought to be younger than the *mare*, and the floor of such a crater should be quite different.

The last of the Rangers will have completed its mission before the equipment for the next step is ready. That step is the "lunar orbiter," a camera-equipped satellite to orbit the moon. Eight lunar orbiters are being built, three for thorough testing on the ground and five for making a strip of the moon along its equator as well known as the *Mare cognitum* is now. The lunar orbiters are expected to weigh about 830 pounds, and the carrier rockets will be Atlas-Agenas, the same that brought Ranger VII to the moon. The planned flight path is along a moon corridor that misses the moon by a little more than six hundred miles. When near the moon the spacecraft will be slowed down so that it will settle into an orbit around the moon. This orbit is expected to be about circular with a distance of 590 miles from the lunar surface.

After this orbit around the moon has been achieved, the rocket motor, which is part of the orbiter, will produce one more slow-down impulse. This will change the nearly circular orbit into an elliptical orbit with a "periselenion" (point nearest the lunar surface) of only twenty-eight miles.

In appearance the lunar orbiter is a circular platform five feet in diameter with a superstructure carrying the camera, transmitter, pressure bottles for attitude-control jets, and the small 100-pound-thrust engine, as well as two antennas, one directional and one omnidirectional. The solar panels are hinged to the bottom platform as in Ranger, but the lunar orbiter has four of them. With folded panels the dimensions are: 5 feet in diameter and 6½ feet in height.

The rocket motor uses a so-called hypergolic combination; this is a system in which the fuel and the oxidizer ignite spontaneously when they are brought together so that there is no need for a separate ignition device.[1] Pressure for the fuel tanks is supplied by the same nitrogen-pressure bottles that feed the attitude-control jets, of which there are eight.

Since the lunar orbiters will be behind the moon as seen from earth, at regular intervals the direct televising of pictures obtained would not be practical. Therefore the lunar orbiters will be equipped with a two-lens-camera system. One lens, or rather set of lenses, is referred to as the low-resolution system. When used from an altitude of twenty-eight miles, the picture will show an area measuring 22.3 by 22.3 miles. The smallest objects showing on this picture will have a diameter of about twenty-five feet. The second lens system, the high-resolution system, will simultaneously photograph the center of this area, producing a picture corresponding to a piece of the lunar surface measuring three by ten miles, but the smallest objects in this picture will have a diameter of only one yard. The camera will hold two hundred feet of seventy-millimeter Kodak SO 243 aerial film. This particular kind of film has been picked because it is not responsive to cosmic

---

[1] The fuel used in this case is a blend of one part ordinary hydrazine and one part unsymmetrical dimethylhydrazine (which ignites more reliably than the ordinary kind), plus nitrogen tetroxide as the oxidizer.

radiation, so it will not be blackened by the passage through the Van Allen belts.

To illustrate the picture-taking capability of the camera system of the lunar orbiter, let us use a terrestrial example. Such an orbiter could photograph all the detail of a mile-wide strip from Philadelphia to Cape Mendocino in California.

The film exposed will be developed before the lunar orbiter has finished one orbit around the moon, and it is then ready for transmission to earth. If only two out of the five planned lunar orbiters function properly, the whole area of the moon where a manned vehicle is going to land later will be known from the high-resolution photographs.

The camera-clicking lunar orbiters will be joined by two other moon-orbiting satellites that will perform other measurements. Their designations are IMP-D and IMP-E, the IMP standing for Interplanetary Monitoring Platform.

The two 215-pound IMP satellites will be made to orbit the moon in such a manner that their periselenion (low point over the moon's surface) will be between three hundred and nine hundred miles, while their aposelenion (high point) will be between two thousand and six thousand miles. The orbital

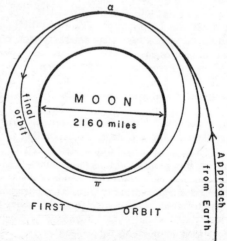

Fig. 30. Lunar Orbiter, Satellite of the Moon. The closest approach at periselenion is about twenty-eight miles but can with luck be as close as twenty miles.

period, depending on what the orbit will be, will vary from five to sixteen hours. As the wide latitude in choice of orbits indicates, these satellites do not investigate the moon itself; they orbit it for the purpose of being carried along by the moon and will therefore always be about 240,000 miles from the earth. These two "moon-anchored" satellites will work in collaboration with two other IMP satellites, namely IMP-F and IMP-G, that will be in orbits around the earth. F and G weigh only 140 pounds each since they lack the retro-rocket system the other two need to assume their moon-anchored orbits. F and G will be in very elongated orbits, with the perigee at about two hundred miles and the apogee as far away as 185,000 miles.

The purpose of the system of four IMP satellites is the investigation of space around the earth, and incidentally around the moon. The IMP satellites will report on the number of micrometeorites in space, the number of charged subatomic particles ("cosmic rays"), and the strength and interplay of magnetic fields in space. But the main point of the investigation—and here the two moon-anchored IMPs are especially important—is something that is called the interplanetary wake of the earth, the "wake" in the solar wind. The term solar wind refers to a steady stream of subatomic particles, consisting of electrons and of protons, that are ejected from the sun and that radiate outward into space in all directions from the sun.

The intensity of this solar wind is known to vary; sometimes the number of electrons and protons ejected is larger than at other times. It is also likely that the composition, that is, the ratio between electrons and protons, is variable. At any event, the magnetic field of the earth acts very much like a rock in a swiftly flowing stream; it diverts the particles around the earth and captures some of them. The result is that for a long distance beyond the earth there is no solar wind, or very little of it, and this particle-free area is the earth's interplanetary wake. The center of this wake is the earth's shadow, but the wake is much wider than the shadow because the wake is produced by the earth's magnetic field, which is naturally much wider than the shadow of the planet. Just how far the wake extends into space is something the four IMP satellites are going to find out.

While the lunar orbiters are still in orbit another step will be taken: Project Surveyor. Surveyor is to be landed on the moon and will send back pictures of its surroundings, along with other information. It will be immobile, remaining in the place where it has landed.[2]

There is a certain amount of "family resemblance" between Surveyor and Ranger, but mainly because a number of the components are the same, or at least look alike. The framework of Surveyor is triangular, and from each corner extends a landing leg terminating in a round plate. Two large solar panels are hinged to a pole that rises from the framework. For the trip through the atmosphere, in the nose cone of the carrier rocket the three landing legs fold upward, while the two solar panels fold downward. Three television cameras are incorporated in the design. One of them points downward—forward, that is, while the spacecraft is approaching the moon—and will be used in the same manner as the cameras in the Ranger. The other two cameras are called the "survey cameras" and will not be used until after landing.

Since the rocket motors of Surveyor have to carry out the midcourse correction as well as accomplish a soft landing against the moon's gravitational pull, there are several of them. Current plans call for a separate retro-rocket package which will do the main slowing down. The retro-rocket package is then to be thrown free of the spacecraft, at which time the altitude of the spacecraft above the lunar surface is expected to be twenty-eight thousand feet and its velocity between three hundred and five hundred feet per second. The rocket motors incorporated in the spacecraft itself only have to kill this velocity, *plus* the velocity that the spacecraft would acquire by falling from a height of twenty-eight thousand feet. It is expected that at an altitude of thirteen feet above the surface the remaining velocity will not be larger than about five feet per second. For the last thirteen feet the spacecraft is going to fall freely, the landing legs will be able to absorb the resulting faint shock.

After landing, various mechanisms will point the high-gain antenna in the direction of the earth, while the solar panels will turn in such a way that their planes are at right angles to the incoming rays of the sun. Since the sun describes only a slow apparent motion in the lunar sky, continuous adjustment of the solar panels is not necessary (as it would be on earth) and current plans call for adjustment of the panels only once every twelve hours. One of the survey cameras will

[2] Project Prospector, a mobile Surveyor (something like the tankette the Russians are talking about), has been dropped as unnecessary. Once a promising landing site has been picked out, exploration by astronauts would be superior in every respect.

be able to photograph a section of the lunar scenery through color filters which are carried in a wheel in front of the camera lens. Changes in picture brightness caused by the different colors of the filters will make it possible to reconstruct the actual colors on earth, but even now every expert is convinced that there is not going to be much color on the moon.

When the sun begins to approach the lunar horizon, most of the power that can still be derived from sunlight will be stored so that all batteries will be fully charged when the long lunar night begins. Then all the systems will go into a hold condition for the duration of darkness and the stored electrical power will be used to maintain an even temperature within the spacecraft.

Preparing for the manned exploration of the moon has a good deal of similarity with other large-scale human activities that engage the skills of many different trades and people. Among activities of the recent past, the planning and building of a large ocean liner probably provides the closest parallel.

When the *Queen Mary* was under construction, the welders and riveters in the shipyard had just started on the framework. But at that time furniture makers were making the furniture that would fit into cabins and salons that were only lines on paper at the moment; artists made sketches of murals that they would paint on walls still to be built; even meat supplies to stock refrigerators still to be purchased and installed were ordered far in advance. Tickets for the first crossing were being sold at the moment, and managers had conferences on who should be appointed captain of the ship-to-be.

The state of Project Apollo at the time Ranger VII took its close-up pictures was something very much like that, except that no tickets for the first crossing were offered for sale or requested by potential passengers.

The rocket designed to carry the Apollo spacecraft did not exist, only its engines did, the large F-1 rocket engines with a takeoff thrust of 1.5 million pounds each. But at Merritt Island, behind Cape Kennedy, ground was broken for the assembly building for the moon rocket, and parts of the enormous crawler vehicle that will carry the rocket from the assembly building to the firing pad were contracted for. The first prototype capsule to be carried by the moon rocket was undergoing tests; scientists held conferences about the scientific equipment to be carried. And astronauts began training.

The landing site on the moon was still to be decided on, for the lunar orbiters were only ordered, but by no means ready. The Surveyor spacecraft which might have the last word in the selection of the landing site had been designed, but it had not even been decided which company would get the order for the retro-rocket package.

However, just as everything flowed together to complete the *Queen Mary* more or less on time, all the activities which have to contribute to, or else precede, Project Apollo will also flow together, presumably also more or less on time.

The unmanned preliminaries of Project Apollo consist of Rangers VII, VIII, and IX, followed by five lunar orbiters and an as yet undetermined number of Surveyors. The manned phase consists of Project Gemini, the two-man capsule put into orbit by the Titan II rocket; simultaneously the rocket for Project Apollo, called Saturn-V, will be developed. The whole program of course culminates in the first manned flight to the moon.

Since all these events are going to overlap, the following timetable will help in visualizing the probable sequence of events. This is not the official timetable but my own opinion

1965

Ranger IX
Final testing of Gemini capsule
First manned Gemini flights
First lunar orbiter

1966

More Gemini flights
More lunar orbiters
First Surveyor
(IMP-D and E)
Air force impact shot
Orbital testing of Apollo components
    (unmanned)

1967

More Gemini flights
More Surveyors
First test flights of Saturn-V (unmanned)
First MOL (?)

1968

Test flights of Saturn-V
Final orbital tests of Apollo capsule
Selection of Apollo crews

of when the various projects are likely to be realized. The year 1969 seems likely as the year in which tests that did not go too well can be repeated. It probably will be the year for tying up loose ends, but if everything goes well, it may also be the year of the moon flight.

But the manned phase still needs to be discussed.

Project Gemini is, in every respect, a prelude to Project Apollo. The two-man capsules of Project Gemini will be put into orbits around the earth, as were the one-man capsules of Project Mercury. But while a Mercury capsule could have supported the life of the astronaut in it for no longer than about thirty-six hours, the Gemini capsules will make orbital flights of a week, two weeks, and even longer, providing all the information that will be needed for long-duration space voyages. This means space voyages after the Apollo flight to the moon, for those astronauts who made a two-and-a-half-week orbital flight in a Gemini capsule will have been in space for a longer time than the astronauts who go to the moon.

The moon-flight maneuver of Project Apollo looks at first glance as if it were too complicated for a first try, but actually it is not, and a careful look at the planned performance shows that it is a fine solution of the problem. The main consideration all the way through is that not a single pound of equipment is carried for a minute longer than it is needed.

The Saturn-V rocket is a three-stage rocket. The bottom stage, called S-IC, stands 137 feet and 6 inches tall and is powered by five kerosene-burning F-1 rocket engines with a combined thrust of 7.5 million pounds. The second stage, called S-II, is 82 feet and 3 inches in length and is powered by five hydrogen-burning J-2 rocket engines with a combined thrust of one million pounds. The third stage, called S-IVB,[3] is 59½ feet in length and is powered by only one J-2 engine. With the Apollo spacecraft perched on top of the whole, the Saturn-V and payload will tower 362 feet over the launch pad.

Takeoff will, of course, be vertical, with a slow eastward tilt being introduced soon after initial liftoff. After 170 seconds, when the fuel supply of the S-IC stage is exhausted, it will be left behind by the S-II stage, which starts burning immediately. As soon as the astronauts in the Apollo space-

---

[3] If the numbering of the stages sounds unusual, it is due to the fact that other stages have been designed so that different combinations can be put together for different missions.

craft are satisfied that the S-II stage is functioning properly, the escape tower will be jettisoned, just as it was done in the Mercury flights, when the escape tower was jettisoned after cutoff of the booster engines of the Atlas rocket. When the second stage is exhausted and jettisoned, the velocity of the third stage and the Apollo spacecraft should be 22,000 feet per second (4.54 miles per second), which is almost, but not quite, enough to stay in orbit around the earth. The remaining small velocity difference will be made up by a brief burst of flame from the engine of the third stage. Then the third stage, with its fuel supply virtually intact, and the Apollo spacecraft will be in a parking orbit one hundred miles or so from the ground.

The total time allotted for staying in the parking orbit is three orbits, or 4½ hours, to allow time for precise tracking and for a final checkout of all equipment. But the spacecraft may complete less than half an orbit—as did Ranger VII— before the third stage is ignited again for insertion into the moon corridor. The velocity in the corridor has to be 35,500 feet per second (6.72 miles per second) when the engine of the third stage is shut off again. The maneuver that follows has been dubbed the transposition maneuver.

To understand what is involved here, the Apollo spacecraft must be described first. It consists of three parts. One is a conical capsule which is *the* spacecraft, where the three astronauts have their living accommodations and where all the controls are located. The name of this portion is command module. The second part is a medium-sized rocket, cylindrical in shape, called the service module. From initial liftoff to insertion into the moon corridor, the service module forms the front end of the whole rocket, with the command module as the nose cone. During this phase of the flight the third part of the Apollo spacecraft is located in the front end of the third stage, that is to say, below the service module. That third part is the one that will actually land on the moon; it has been named LEM, from lunar-excursion module. But if the three sections of the Apollo spacecraft were left in these relative positions, no midcourse correction could be made, because the LEM would be in the way of the exhaust of the service module. The relative position of the three sections must be rearranged, and that is the transposition maneuver.

The command and service modules will be pulled away from the third stage, which still holds the LEM, and then will turn around. The tip of the conical command module will make contact with the LEM, and when the LEM is firmly attached, retro-rockets *attached to the third stage* will be fired. This slows down the third stage, with the result that the LEM, now connected to the command module, will be pulled away from it. At the end of the transposition maneuver the Apollo spacecraft is complete, with the LEM on top of the command module and the command module on top of the service module. Both the complete spacecraft and the third stage will be on their way to the moon, but the third stage, slowed down by its retro-rockets, will lag behind. Of course the spacecraft will be traveling "backward," with the exhaust nozzle of the service module pointing in the direction of motion, but that fact is unimportant at the moment. It remains unimportant for many hours to come.

The captain of the spacecraft has a great deal of leeway here. Since the Apollo spacecraft does not depend on sunlight for its electrical power, its attitude on the flight path is a minor matter until the time for the midcourse correction comes near. The midcourse correction will probably involve a speeding up of the ship. But it *can* involve a slowdown, since the ship could be somewhat too fast. It is entirely conceivable that the captain may decide to let the ship travel tail first until he is certain that it is a speedup that is needed and not a slowdown. Of course, more than one midcourse correction might be made. (The word "midcourse" must not be taken literally; it just means a correction while in transit.)

At the moment three midcourse corrections are built into the tentative flight plan, one seventeen hours after insertion into the moon corridor, one forty-four hours after insertion, when the spacecraft actually is about midway to the moon, and a final one after sixty-eight hours, which is just before the spacecraft goes into orbit around the moon. The total velocity change caused by the midcourse corrections is expected to be minor, not more than three hundred feet per second. The next major maneuver after insertion into the moon corridor is the slowdown in the vicinity of the moon.

The intended orbit is circular and ninety miles from the moon's surface, and the orbital velocity required happens to be almost precisely one mile per second. Therefore the rocket engine of the service module must eliminate the excess above one mile per second. Even if we had telescopes which would enable us to see the Apollo spacecraft when it is near the moon, we could not see this maneuver because it will begin about fifteen minutes after Apollo has passed behind the moon. The orbital period is two hours, and it is expected that the spacecraft goes through at least one complete orbit before the next maneuver—the preparation for the actual landing—begins.

Two of the three astronauts will leave the command module and enter the LEM, which will be ready for the landing maneuver because it has traveled in ready position, with all four landing legs extended, all along. After the two astronauts are settled in the cabin of the landing module, it will be disconnected and the astronauts will wait for the moment to start their slowdown maneuver. Just when this will be depends on the landing site that has been chosen. The first slowdown of the LEM must begin when it is over that point of the lunar surface which is precisely antipodal to the landing site. The first slowdown amounts to only eighty-eight feet per second, but that will result in an elliptical orbit (resembling that of the lunar orbiters) with its periselenion fifty thousand feet above the landing site. There the second slowdown starts, which brings the LEM to a point two hundred feet above the landing site, where it hovers. From then on the pilot of the LEM lands it under manual control. The coasting descent from orbit to periselenion takes one hour, from there to hovering takes eight minutes, and the time allotted for the manual-controlled descent to touchdown is two minutes. Meanwhile the service module and the command module, with one astronaut in it, stays in orbit around the moon, acting as a relay satellite between the landing party and earth.

This is the reason why the first landing must be made near the lunar equator. The Apollo spacecraft, coming from earth, will assume an orbit roughly coinciding with the equator. If the LEM lands near the equator, the orbiting spacecraft will be in radio range of the landing party for nearly one half of its orbital period. But if the LEM had landed far from the equator, the time available for communication would be a much smaller fraction of each orbit. Landing near the equator simplifies the whole procedure, even though the temperature of the ground could theoretically pose a major problem. This problem can be avoided, however, by landing soon after sunrise on the landing site.

It is expected that one of the two astronauts who have landed will be inside the LEM, while the other one is out on the surface. Total duration of stay on the moon is quite flexible; it can be as short as four hours or as long as forty-four hours.

The LEM consists of two parts, which might be called capsule and undercarriage. The capsule consists of the cabin, with all communications equipment, fuel tanks, and rocket engine, and the undercarriage is a supporting structure with the landing legs. The undercarriage serves as launch platform for the capsule when the time has come to return to orbit. After the upper part of the LEM has made rendezvous with

TIMETABLE FOR FIRST APOLLO FLIGHT TO THE MOON

	MINIMUM	MAXIMUM
Time in parking orbit	1 hour	4½ hours
Transit time in moon corridor	2½ days	3 days
Orbit around the moon (LEM operations)	½ day (6 hours)	7 days (46 hours)
Return to earth	3½ days	4½ days
Total	6½ days	14½ days

the orbiting units, the specimens collected on the moon will be transferred to the command module. Then the two astronauts will enter the command module and the rocket engine of the service module will insert the service and command modules into the earth corridor, the return flight. The upper part of the LEM will be left in orbit around the moon; it is possible that some equipment will be incorporated into the capsule of the LEM that will make it useful as a communications satellite for later landing parties.

The velocity required for insertion into the earth corridor is eighty-one hundred feet per second. Since the orbiting spacecraft already moves at the rate of fifty-three hundred feet per second, only twenty-eight hundred feet per second need to be added.

There will be midcourse corrections on the return flight too. Five minutes before reentry into the earth's atmosphere the command module is separated from the service module so that only the command module reenters and returns to the ground. The first mission to the moon will have been completed.

Because only the service module is left when the mission is over, the question of what has happened to the other parts of the 362-foot rocket that took off from Merritt Island two weeks before is justified.

The most bulky part of the whole, the first stage, will have fallen back into the atmosphere and crashed somewhere in the ocean, unless, as is hoped, ways and means have been found in the meantime to recover the first stage for reuse. The second stage and the jettisoned escape tower will be short-lived satellites of the earth and burn up on reentry. The third stage will have slipped out of the moon corridor because of insufficient velocity, will have missed the moon, and will be in orbit around the sun. Of the LEM, the lower part will have been left on the moon and the upper part will stay in orbit around the moon. As for the service module, there are two possibilities. It might reenter the atmosphere at a different point from the reentry corridor of the command module and burn up, or else it might pass the earth without touching atmosphere and then go into an orbit around the sun.

Has anybody looked beyond Apollo? Yes, but not in great detail, because any detailed thinking that is done now will most likely be changed by developments that take place during the next five or six years. Designers are thinking hard about things that we now know will be needed, especially a surface vehicle for getting around on the surface of the moon. Before the twentieth century comes to an end there will be at least one base on the moon, and even if there is only one it will consist of several installations, such as an astronomical observatory (with both optical and radio telescopes), research laboratories taking advantage of the moon's airlessness and lesser gravity, and crew's quarters.

Just how these installations will look will largely be determined by the first Apollo mission. But it is certain that they will take shape, in one form or another, before more than a quarter century has gone by.

Appendixes

The Main Facts About Our Moon

Dimensions:

Diameter	(0.2722 that of earth)	2,160 miles
Diameter	(apparent, as seen from earth)	
	max. 33 minutes 30 seconds of arc	
	min. 29 minutes 21 seconds of arc	
	mean 31 minutes 5 seconds of arc	
Circumference		6,785 miles
Surface area	(0.075 that of earth)	14,600,000 square miles
Volume	(0.020 that of earth)	5,260 million cubic miles

Orbit:

Distance	(center to center)	max. (apogee)	252,710 miles
		min. (perigee)	221,463 miles
		mean	238,857 miles
Length of major axis			475,000 miles
Eccentricity			0.055

Orbital velocity
    max. (perigee) 2,470 m.p.h. (0.686 miles per second)
    min. (apogee) 2,160 m.p.h. (0.60   miles per second)
    mean   2,287 m.p.h. (0.63   miles per second)

Orbital period (sidereal, relative to fixed stars)
            27 days, 7 hours, 43 minutes, 11.5 seconds

Inclination of lunar orbit to ecliptic, mean
        5 degrees, 8 minutes, 43 seconds of arc

Other data:

Period of rotation	same as orbital period
Motion of point at lunar equator	10.5 miles per hour
Surface gravity (earth=1)	0.16
Density (earth=1)	0.6
Density (water=1)	3.35

Mass
  (1/81.56 that of earth)   81,000,000,000,000 million tons
Inclination of lunar
  equator to lunar orbit   1 degree, 32 minutes of arc
Escape velocity   1.5 miles per second
Circular velocity   1.06 miles per second
Albedo   0.07

Chronology of United States Attempts to Reach the Moon

August 17, 1958 *Thor-Able* rocket carrying lunar probe. At
    77 seconds after takeoff engine failure in the first stage
    caused explosion of the rocket.

October 11, 1958 *Thor-Able* rocket carrying lunar probe
    called *Pioneer I*. Upper stage failed to develop the neces-
    sary velocity, probe rose to a total altitude of 71,300
    miles, then fell back. Reentered atmosphere over South
    Pacific 43 hours and 17.5 minutes after takeoff.

November 8, 1958 *Thor-Able* rocket carrying lunar probe
    Pioneer II. Third stage failed to ignite, probe reached a
    peak altitude of 963 miles, reentered atmosphere 42.4
    minutes after takeoff, falling into the Atlantic Ocean.

December 6, 1958 *Juno* rocket (*Jupiter* missile with extra
    upper stages) carried lunar probe *Pioneer III*, intended
    to be a near-miss. Upper stages did not achieve sufficient
    velocity, maximum altitude reached was 66,654 miles.
    Discovered outer Van Allen belt, reentered over equato-
    rial Africa 38 hours and 6 minutes after takeoff.

March 3, 1959 *Juno* rocket carrying lunar probe *Pioneer IV*,
    intended to be a near-miss. Passed moon at a distance
    of 37,300 miles, too far away for the instruments to
    collect any information. After passing moon, the probe
    went into orbit around the sun.

September 10, 1959 *Atlas-Able I*. Lunar probe exploded on
    launching pad.

November 26, 1959 *Atlas-Able II*. Lunar probe showed per-
    fect takeoff but lost nose-cone shroud during climb and
    exploded in midair 45 seconds after ignition.

September 25, 1960 *Atlas-Able III*. Upper stages failed to
    produce enough velocity, vehicle fell back and burned
    up during reentry.

December 15, 1960 *Atlas-Able IV* exploded at 40,000 feet
    within full view of the launching crew and other spec-
    tators.

August 23, 1961 *Atlas-Agena B* rocket carrying lunar probe.
    Ranger I. Upper stage failed to work, vehicle climbed
    to 120 miles, then fell back.

November 18, 1961 *Atlas-Agena B* rocket carrying lunar probe. *Ranger II*. Same fate as *Ranger I*.

January 26, 1962 *Atlas-Agena B* rocket carrying lunar probe. *Ranger III*, intended to impact moon. Missed moon by 23,000 miles and went into orbit around the sun. Orbital period is 406.4 days, perihelion of orbit is 91,503,000 miles from the sun, aphelion is at a distance of 108,134,-000 miles from the sun. (The perihelion of earth is 91,500,000 miles from the sun, the aphelion lies at 94,500,000 miles; the orbit of the probe is, therefore, somewhat larger than the earth's orbit.)

April 23, 1962 *Atlas-Agena B* rocket carrying *Ranger IV*. Spacecraft malfunctioned and tumbled, missed moon's leading edge by 900 miles, impacted on the moon's far side. No pictures obtained.

October 18, 1962 *Atlas-Agena B* rocket carrying *Ranger V*. Probe was to pass the moon at a distance of a few hundred miles, take TV pictures, and eject capsule which was to impact on the moon. Because of electrical power failure soon after takeoff, nothing worked. Spacecraft passed moon at a distance of 450 miles on October 20 and went into an orbit around the sun quite similar to the orbit of *Ranger III*.

January 30, 1964 *Atlas-Agena B* rocket carried *Ranger VI*. Perfect trajectory to the moon with impact in the vicinity of the crater Arago. But the TV cameras on board the spacecraft failed to work, hence no results.

July 28, 1964 *Atlas-Agena B* rocket carried *Ranger VII*. Impact on moon near crater Guericke 68½ hours after takeoff. Cameras worked, full success.

February 17, 1965 *Atlas-Agena B* rocket carried *Ranger VIII*. Impact in the area of the *Mare tranquillitatis* on February 20 at 4:47:36.8 A.M. (E.S.T.), transmitting close to 7,500 photographs during the last twenty-three minutes of flight. Full success.

Chronology of Soviet Attempts to Reach the Moon

January 2, 1959 Russian *CH-10* rocket (takeoff thrust estimated at 660,000 pounds) carried space probe *Metchtá* ("Daydream"), which passed moon at a distance of 4,600 miles. Radio signals stopped a few hours after crossing the moon's orbit, suggesting that probe had been fired for impact. In orbit around sun, period is 447 days, perihelion at 90,968,000 miles, aphelion at 122,535,000 miles.

September 12, 1959 Unspecific "multistage rocket" (very

likely quite similar to the three-stage *CH-10*) carried lunar probe weighing about 860 pounds for impact in the area of *Mare serenitatis*. Probe traveled 236,875 miles in 35 hours and struck, according to Russian scientists, about 160 miles from the intended target area. Impact velocity estimated at 10,900 feet per second. Tracked on both September 12 and 13 by British Jodrell Bank radio-telescope.

October 4, 1959 Artificial satellite *1959 Theta,* in elongated orbit which looped behind the moon, succeeded in taking several pictures of portions of the moon not visible from earth.

January 4, 1963 Lunar probe was put into parking orbit around the earth, but the orbiting top stage failed to ignite and has probably reentered the atmosphere and burned up since then.

February 5, 1963 Lunar probe took off to go into parking orbit, but the first stage of the rocket failed to produce the necessary velocity. Spacecraft fell into the Pacific Ocean near Midway Island.

April 2, 1963 Lunar probe labeled *Moon IV* and weighing 3,135 pounds was fired from parking orbit. Western experts think that a soft landing on the moon was intended. Probe missed moon by 5,300 miles and went into orbit around the sun. Orbital data unknown.

Some Books About the Moon

Asimov, Isaac. *The Double Planet.* New York: Abelard-Schuman, Limited, 1960. A popular book on the earth considered as a planet, the moon, and their mutual interactions, such as tides.

Baldwin, Ralph B. *The Face of the Moon.* Chicago: University of Chicago Press, 1949. A valuable book devoted mainly to problems of crater formation by impact. Somewhat technical in places, but not too difficult for the interested reader who has read one or two introductory books.

Fielder, Gilbert. *Structure of the Moon's Surface.* New York and London: Pergamon Press, 1961. A condensation of all research results up to the time of writing. Well illustrated and highly interesting, but requires a great deal of background knowledge.

Firsoff, V. A. *Strange World of the Moon.* New York: Basic Books, Inc., Publishers, 1959. An account of all the lunar phenomena, based on a thorough and detailed study.

————. *Surface of the Moon: Its Structure and Origin*. London: Hutchinson & Co., Ltd., 1961. More specialized than the former, dealing mainly with the surface features.

Ley, Willy. *Watchers of the Skies*. New York: The Viking Press, Inc., Publishers, 1963. A general history of astronomy; the historical aspects of selenography are treated in Chapter XI, "Earth and Vicinity."

Markov, A. V. (ed.). *The Moon—A Russian View*. Chicago: University of Chicago Press, 1962. An English translation of studies by Russian lunar experts. Technical, not for the beginner.

Moore, Patrick. *A Guide to the Moon*. New York: W. W. Norton & Company, Inc., Publishers, 1953. A well-written general account of our moon, a useful introduction for beginners.

————. *A Survey of the Moon*. New York: W. W. Norton & Company, Inc., Publishers, 1963. Also written for the general reader, but slanted toward the needs of amateur astronomers who wish to observe the moon.

Nasmyth, James, and James Carpenter. *The Moon: Considered as a Planet, a World, and a Satellite*. London, 1874. A large quarto-size book with beautiful illustrations. Though obsolete in many respects, it is still worth reading, if only for historical reasons.

Neison, Edmund. *The Moon and the Condition and Configurations of Its Surface*. London, 1876. A thick volume of 576 pages, "the first of the English classics," as Patrick Moore calls it. A detailed description, with charts, of the whole lunar surface.

Richardson, Robert S. (ed.). *Man and the Moon*. New York: The World Publishing Company, 1961. A collection of writings on the moon, by American and British astronomers, for the general reader. Illustrations by Chesley Bonestell.

Sykes, J. B. (trans.). *The Other Side of the Moon*. New York and London: Pergamon Press, 1960. An English translation of the book issued by the U.S.S.R. Academy of Science describing the flight and the results of Cosmic Rocket III, which took pictures of portions of the moon's far side.

Wilkins, H. Percy. *Our Moon*. London: Frederick Muller, Ltd., Publishers, 1954. Highly readable introduction to the lunar world; this small book might be called a "first reader" in selenology.

Other SIGNET SCIENCE LIBRARY Books

60¢ Each

THIS IS OUTER SPACE   **by Lloyd Motz**

A concise explanation of modern scientists' most recent discoveries about the nature of the universe. (#P2084)

SEEING THE EARTH FROM SPACE   **by Irving Adler**

A timely, up-to-date report on Russian and American Satellites and what we are learning from them about our earth. Illustrated.   (#P2050)

NEW HANDBOOK OF THE HEAVENS
       **by Hubert J. Bernhard, Dorothy A. Bennett,
and Hugh S. Rice**

A guide to the understanding and enjoyment of astronomy for beginners as well as the more advanced, with star charts and data, descriptions of the heavenly bodies, and astronomical facts and lore.   (#P2123)

THE WORLD OF COPERNICUS (Sun, Stand Thou Still)
                           by Angus Armitage

The biography of the great astronomer of the 15th and 16th centuries who established the general plan of the solar system which we can accept today.   (#P2370)

THE SUN AND ITS FAMILY   **by Irving Adler**

A popular book on astronomy which traces scientific discoveries about the solar system from earliest times to the present. Illustrated.   (#P2037)

THE STARS   **by Irving Adler**

A clear introduction to the nature, motion, and structure of the stars.   (#P2093)

HOW LIFE BEGAN   **by Irving Adler**

A readable account of what science has discovered about the origin of life. Preface by Linus Pauling. Illustrated.   (#P2135)